Foreword

By Gerry Murph·
President of the Irish Congre·

It gives me great pleasure to co   ond
working-class writing project initi.

In 1909 James Larkin founded "One .   ..sport & General
Workers' Union (ITGWU). Soon aft   .veekly newspaper, the
Irish Worker, used the arts to comple.   .ɔ socialist message, publishing
not only cartoons, but also poetry and prose, even short plays. The ITGWU
recognised the importance of waging the cultural battle alongside the
economic, social and political ones, and the Irish labour movement today
continues this important tradition. James Connolly himself was also a prolific
writer of songs and ballads, underlying his appreciation of the power of
communicating with workers in a creative and artistic idiom.

I am proud that trade union organisations from the whole island of Ireland
have been instrumental in sponsoring this project of anthologies of working
people's writing. I sincerely thank all those unions, which have supported this
venture, in a common understanding of the value of the working-class voice
being heard.

It is also apt, in the midst of the Covid-19 pandemic, that the true value and
critical importance of workers' contributions to our communities, worldwide,
takes centre stage. These contributions expose the parasitical captains of
industry and their fellow travellers in global finance. The disproportionate
impact of the pandemic on working-class, ethnic minority and other
disadvantaged communities confirms the need to fight for fundamental
change to the political and economic structures of society and to achieve
this we must struggle on a multitude of fronts. This publication, I believe,
represents an essential element in our overall fight to advance the interests
of the working class, and I commend it to all of you.

Introduction

By Jenny Farrell, Department of Languages & Humanities, Galway-Mayo Institute of Technology and Associate Editor, Culture Matters

Culture Matters has undertaken to publish the voices of working people in Ireland, not simply as individual authors, but as an *anthology* of writings from a working person's point of view. In November 2019, we published the first of these anthologies, *The Children of the Nation*, which immediately sold out. It is a collection of contemporary poetry from a wide range of working people, across the whole of Ireland.

This second volume focuses on prose, both short fiction and life writing. As with the first collection, we reached out to potential contributors through writers' social networks, trade unions, and word of mouth. The trade union movement in Ireland grasps the central importance of the cultural struggle in improving the lives of working people, and we are proud of and very grateful for its solidarity and support for this pioneering project to publish the first anthologies of working people's writings from contemporary Ireland.

In mainstream culture, the ruling class, through the cultural establishment, determines the narrative. It exercises cultural hegemony, which complements its economic exploitation and political domination. When collecting material for these first anthologies of working people's writings, contributors commented that their own life experience motivated their writing, because they did not find characters like themselves in literature. While awareness has grown, it speaks volumes that these anthologies are the first of their kind in Ireland. Publishing working people's voices together in an anthology takes a stand against the mainstream narrative, mainstream educational assumptions, and mainstream cultural sidelining.

In his poem 'A Worker Reads and Asks Questions', Bertolt Brecht highlights the kind of story we do not encounter in the history books—the role of ordinary, working people in the historical process:

Who built seven-gated Thebes
In the books you'll find the names of kings.
Was it the kings that lugged those hunks of rock?
And what of Babylon, so often demolished?
Who rebuilt it time and again? In which
Of golden Lima's houses lived its builders?
On the day the Chinese Wall was finished where

From the Plough to the Stars

An Anthology of Working People's Prose from Contemporary Ireland

Edited and introduced by
Jenny Farrell

Foreword by Gerry Murphy

Jenny Farrell

B'fhada uaithi cuimhniú ach oiread gurb é an Duine ba chiontach leis an lear léanmhar a choinnigh in adhastar an anró agus amhgair í, ...a choinnigh faoi shíor imní agus ag síorsclábhaíocht í.

She was far from realising that man, not Providence, was answerable to the sea of troubles which confined her to struggle and skimp, sent her tramping every Saturday to Brightcity barefoot, left her worrying always, slaving all the time.

—Máirtín Ó Cadhain (1906-1970)

First published in 2020 by **Culture Matters** Co-Operative Ltd.
Culture Matters promotes a socialist and progressive approach to art,
culture and politics. See www.culturematters.org.uk

Acknowledgements

Culture Matters is grateful for the support and assistance of INTO, the Irish
National Teachers' Organisation; USDAW, the Union of Shop, Distributive
and Allied Workers; the National Education Union; and the Cork and
Fermanagh Trades Councils.

Irish National Teachers' Organisation
Cumann Múinteoiri Éireann

Union of Shop, Distributive
and Allied Workers

Cork Council of Trade Unions
Comhairle Cheardchumann Chorcai

FERMANAGH COUNCIL OF TRADES UNIONS

ENNISKILLEN TRADES & LABOUR COUNCIL
ESTABLISHED 1919

Did the masons go in the evening? Great Rome
Is full of triumphal arches. Who raised them? Over whom
Did the Caesars triumph? Had Byzantium of the songs
Palaces only, for its inhabitants? Even in fabulous Atlantis,
The very night the sea swallowed it,
The drowning still bawled for their slaves.

Young Alexander conquered India.
All alone?
Caesar defeated the Gauls.
Didn't he have so much as a cook with him?
Phillip of Spain wept when his fleet
Sank. Did no others shed tears?
Frederick the Second won the Seven Years' War.
Who else?

A victory on every page.
Who cooked the victory feast?
A great man every ten years.
Who paid the bill?

So many accounts.
So many questions.

(translation: Jack Mitchell)

It is apparent to working people, not only in Ireland, that history fails to record their experience. Instead, the thrust of history writing is determined by the paymaster's point of view, which excludes the perspective of those who fight and die, who do the work, who dream of and struggle for a better life. Apart from establishment history, there is the story of the working people, and so, distinct from the mainstream, there is a second culture, reflecting the working-class experience. To hear the voice of ordinary people of the past, we must resort to the non-mainstream spheres of folk songs, folktales, and folk-art, which preserve this experience. What we find here are not the stereotypes of working people typical of ruling-class literature and art, but real characters: not the pastoral, but the anti-pastoral.

When in the Renaissance a new artisan and trader class slowly replaced the aristocracy as the ruling class, they produced their own artists. The most famous of these are: the son of a glover, William Shakespeare; the son of a bricklayer, Ben Jonson; and the son of a shoemaker, Christopher Marlowe.

They were not part of the ruling aristocratic elite, and broke new ground both socially and artistically. Two hundred years later, establishment critics mocked the apothecary John Keats, asserting an inferior quality of working people's writing. Other common people poets from that time of revolutions are the son of a tenant farmer, Robert Burns, the son of a hosier, William Blake, and the agricultural labourer from childhood, John Clare.

In Ireland, the small farmer and hedge-schoolteacher Brian Merriman stands out as a poet. In 'Cúirt An Mheán Oíche' ('The Midnight Court'), ahead of the United Irishmen, he declares a new age, where the women will free Ireland. And in 19th and 20th century Ireland, there are Ethna Carbery, Liam O' Flaherty, Mary Ellen Cregan, Seán O'Casey, Maeve Cavanagh, Pádraic Ó Conaire, Madge Herron, Peadar O'Donnell, Máirtín Ó Cadhain, Juanita Casey, Seosamh Mac Grianna, Máirtín Ó Direáin, Linda Anderson, Patrick Kavanagh, Frank O'Connor and many others, who described the lives of the ordinary people, only for their work to be frequently ridiculed, even banned by the establishment. It is in this proud tradition we root our anthologies.

Our understanding of the 'working class' are those people who sell their labour power and share only marginally in the fruits of their labour. They create the basis of national wealth, yet their living conditions are frequently precarious. Far from disappearing, the working class is growing in size, regardless of the nature of their employment. It comprises not only people in traditional working-class employment, and small farmers, but also the many who find themselves unemployed, self-employed, or in precarious employment, part-time hours, zero-hours contracts, low pay, unemployed and homeless—all driven into a poverty trap. As 'Social Justice Ireland' states in its most recent report (reflecting 2018 statistics), prior 'to the current public health crisis, one in every seven people in Ireland lived below the poverty line; about 680,000 people... these numbers look set to rise as the very uneven impact of the Covid-19 crisis unfolds.'

About 200,000 children lived in households that were experiencing poverty. The organisation further confirms that having a job is not, of itself, a protection against poverty. In 2018, almost 110,000 *employed* workers lived below the poverty line. The social divide is growing, disproving the establishment myth that nearly everybody is 'middle class'. This notion not only implies that being working class is unacceptable, it also creates a smokescreen designed to prevent a challenge to the system.

In this sense, it is in keeping with our understanding of second culture that all authors who identify with the condition of the working class, who share in this experience and articulate it, should be part of our project.

The contributors to this new anthology are very aware of social injustice, the erosion of their living and working conditions. In fifty contributions, both factual life writing and rooted-in-life fiction and images, they explore the condition of working people in contemporary Ireland, north and south, east and west, rural and urban, female and male, in Irish and in English.

As with the previous anthology, we asked contributors to provide a short biography along with their submission. These biographies are a kind of life writing in their own right, something to be read with interest along with the submitted text. It is unsurprising that education is an important theme in many biographies and contributions, the contributors frequently being the first generation of a working-class family to have had access to secondary and college education.

Education is also a theme of empowerment in the texts, perhaps most notably in Linda Ervine's 'Education'. Several contributors noted that mainstream education presented them with distorted images of the working class and implied that a degree meant they were no longer working class. This suggests that working-class people by definition cannot be educated—an arrogant assumption that disregards the relationship between labour and remuneration. It also highlights the enormous task ahead, for the working class to determine how it is represented in education, culture and the media.

It is striking also how many stories include the theme of the Irish language as a point of cultural identification. Frequently, this is linked to class identification: take Tomás Mac Síomóin's story of Irish classes in Ballyfermot in 'A Ballyfermot Enigma!', or Eoin Ó Murchú's 'Cuimhní'/ 'Memory' about the importance Irish had for his development. Linda Ervine, Irish Language Development Officer in the heart of East Belfast, mentions Irish as part of the new worlds opened to her by education. Andy Snoddy ('The Radical Protestant Tradition') echoes the importance of Irish for Protestants on this island, as well as highlighting the significance of the Protestant tradition in the fight for Irish independence. Both these aspects resurface in Brian Campfield's memoir 'O'Donnell Holds Court'.

Writing in Irish, two women authors, Máire Dinny Wren ('Cosmhuintir'/ 'The Common People') and Celia de Fréine ('Caoi leis an Ord Tábhachta a chaitheamh i dTraipisí?'/ 'A Way in Which to Overturn the Pecking Order?'), employ pared-down parables, connecting past storytelling tone with the present. Celia de Fréine's reference to the pandemic in terms of a brief breaking-up of class rule, of the true importance of the working people becoming outstandingly obvious, is linked to other tales of pandemic experience. They include the chaos described by Rosemary Jenkinson in 'This Year is Cancelled', a diary entry by frontline nurse Bernadette Murphy, and Anita Gracey's poignant farewell to her brother Brian, 'Sketch of an Atheist'. Attracta Fahy explores 'Mothering through the Pandemic'. Ross Walsh's 'King of the Concrete Jungle' follows the deadly virus into a post-human world. The eeriness of lockdown has suggested to others the realities of an ecological catastrophe, as explored in Stephen James Douglas's 'Gaia's Diagnosis'. Existential fear of the kind linked to serious illness features in some texts, for example in Paul Jeffcutt's 'Sixteen Tons'.

As was the case in the first anthology, the violence experienced in working-class estates, poverty, drug abuse, alcoholism and moneylending feature here too. These themes inform the stark short stories by Karl Parkinson ('Deano And The Boys From The Block: Word portrait of an inner city youth'), Declan Geraghty ('Nine Hour Stroll'), Edward Boyne ('Local'). Sinéad Cameron's image 'Worker Dispenser' underlines the perceived dispensability of working people. They show a reality that urgently demands that the state take its responsibility for all its citizens seriously. The absence of a duty of care from all sides is also at the heart of Patrick Bolger's Memoir 'Revelation', revealing clerical sexual abuse of children.

In some accounts, resilience to adversity emerges, for example in Rachael Hegarty's 'The Dodgy Box', or the hope to reunite family over Gaelic football in Gráinne Daly's 'The Dublin-Meath Saga'. Seamus Scanlon brings dark humour to resistance in his flash fiction thriller 'On the House', as does Mary Lennon ('Taken by a Gangsta'). Dave Lordan also presents the reader with dark short fiction located in a disturbing setting. Liz Gillis ('The Liberties: We Don't Eat Our Young Here Anymore') and Geri Slevin ('Sea Gypsy'), on the other hand, emphasise the strength they gained from growing up in working-class estates. Maeve McKenna also roots a sense of home just here ('I Want to go Home').

Some writers project a harsh reality into a dystopia, as Frank Murphy's 'Welcome to Dystopia', or Camillus John's 'The Rise and Fall of Cinderella's Left Testicle'. There is also a retrospective dystopia shown as one possible outcome of WWII, had Germany won, in David Murphy's 'Token House', exploring a class-ridden society, not so far removed from contemporary reality.

From a dystopian future to a dystopian past, emigration and homelessness are themes that featured prominently in the poetry collection, and continue here. These appear in Mícheál Ó hAodha's 'Imithe'/ 'Gone' and Bern Butler's 'A Tale of Two Cities 1985'. Victoria McNulty ('White Horses') also writes eloquently about emigration in terms of the effects on the lives of those born into it. Emigration and holding on to identity is also the theme of Eoin Ó Murchú's memoir.

Set during the troubles in Belfast, Brian Campfield writes about the need for working-class unity and shows how this was achieved for a moment in honour of the legendary Peadar O'Donnell. British military violence, occurring at the same time in Belfast, feature in Seán Maguire's 'Window Pain', a chilling story based on personal experience, and the long-term effect of sectarian thinking is evoked in John D. Kelly's 'Meandering'.

Prejudice of different kinds are explored, be it middle-class aloofness by Jennifer Horgan ('Their Daughter's Bib'), Lani O'Hanlon ('If you were the only girl') and Michael Casey ('Fadings'), and chauvinism towards Travellers in Alan O'Brien's 'Culture'. In these stories, we have not only the author's critical viewpoint but also find more enlightened characters who take class-conscious positions.

Both female and male contributors write about themes centred on women. Barbara O'Donnell ('Thresholds') interweaves her own experience as an Irish woman with that of her mother. Linda Ervine's memoir shows how she broke free from humiliation and violence and achieved self-determination. Many writers highlight an understanding that the working people need to stand together in solidarity to overcome injustice and discrimination. Moya Roddy shows the growing strength of the 'weak' in 'They also serve who only...'. Anne Waters ('St. Stephen's Day') recalls the trauma of the Magdalen Laundries and in 'Evelyn' Jim Ward writes in the voice of a Polish waitress in an homage to Joyce's 'Eveline'. Solidarity with eastern European workers, to the point of adopting their voice, in this case male, also features in Alan Weadick's 'Transcendence'.

These writers from the whole island of Ireland create a complex image of Irish working people today, one that challenges middle-class stereotypes of their class. The voice that emerges in this anthology, as it did in *The Children of the Nation*, is intelligent, eloquent, aware of the profound injustice of the working-class condition, and able and willing to fight back. Solidarity and fightback are the main themes in Seosamh Ó Cuaig's memoir 'Stailc Suiminte 1970'/ 'The 1970 Cement Strike', in Andy Snoddy's memoir, or in James O'Brien's story ('Rebel Meg') of more surreptitious resistance. Anne Mac Darby-Beck writes about how class prejudice causes her to revolt in 'Sick Day', and Moya Roddy looks at how class understanding is a growing realisation. The fight against water rates, which is the setting for Moya's story, reappears in Kevin Doyle's 'The Water War' and Kevin Higgins' satirical blog 'Vigil in support of Irish Water during Seanad vote on Wednesday'.

The stories gathered here cannot be reduced to single ideas. They cut across a variety of themes, as does a working person's experience, and we mention them only to indicate the scope and statement of the anthology as a whole. In this way, *From the Plough to the Stars* continues the testimonial of *The Children of the Nation* poetry anthology, changing 'his story' to 'our story' in the spirit of Bertolt Brecht.

The texts contained in this collection present us not with an individual hero/ine, but with a diverse set of characters who combine, like a mosaic, into a group hero/ine. Each has something to contribute, the whole being greater than the sum of its parts. It is a group that will ultimately rise above the inferior station assigned to them by society, and who will seek to create a just society for all. In the words of James Connolly describing the Starry Plough banner:

A free Ireland will control its own destiny, from the plough to the stars.

Contents

Patrick Bolger

is a writer and visual artist. His writing gives voice to issues often silenced and marginalised in Irish society—including childhood sexual violence and the corrosive impact that childhood trauma, when met with silence at a familial, community and societal level, can have on both the individual and the collective. It explores themes of self-identity, addiction, mental health, masculinity, love and relationships.

Born into a working-class family in rural County Wicklow, Patrick was the first in his family to attend college. Social justice and the role of privilege in creating class divisions and prejudices in society are also explored in his work.

Revelation

It's August 1998. Having just returned from ten days working in a hot and humid Budapest, I am sitting in my parents' house drinking tea with my mother. *The Irish Independent* sits on the kitchen table. My mother is standing by the cooker. My father is outside in his garden. His safe place when I visit, and maybe his safe place when alone with my mother.

The windows on both sides of the kitchen extension, built by my father, let the wind blow through. I am tired. I will drink my tea and get on the road, my duty done. I open the paper, half in conversation, half in flight. Turn the pages. Scan them. I turn another page. Page 5. Page 6. Page 7. Page 8. Page 9. I stop. My body frozen.

I don't remember driving across the bridge with him. I don't remember what he said to me. I don't remember how he was with me. I know we went to the church, the sacristy where babies would be christened. He parked outside and we walked through the small gate, around the back into the sacristy. It was quiet. We were early. He opened the door and closed it behind us. The smell, I remember the smell. It was old, cold. A little damp.

The paint peeling off the walls. Cold candles waiting to be relit. Wax. A sink. His chair.

I am staring at his photograph in the paper. Tom Naughton. Fr. Thomas Naughton. Being escorted from court after being convicted of the sexual abuse of Mervyn Rundle in Donneycarney in 1985. I hadn't seen his face since 1982. Sixteen years. It was all I remembered it to be. And more. I said something to my mother. Cursed. That's him. The bastard. Or something like that. I don't remember her saying or doing anything. I don't remember her putting her hand on my shoulder or over her mouth. I don't remember her asking me was I okay? In twenty years, nothing had changed. When I was eight years old, driving in the tractor with my father, he stopped and asked me did the priest play games with me? I said yes. He never mentioned it again.

I reversed out of the driveway and drove over the bridge, back to Valleymount.

There were three christenings that day. I would be alone with him for the whole day. Later, in a small brown envelope, there would be some money for me. Notes. From the christening families (or him, who knows?) for the altar boy. Maybe it made him feel better to pay me. Maybe it cleared his conscience.

During the christening he would mark the baby's head. Chrism. Wet his head. Water. Then the renewal of vows.

V. Do you reject Satan?

R. I do.

V. And all his works?

R. I do.

V. And all his empty promises?

R. I do.

V. Do you believe in God, the Father Almighty, Creator of heaven and earth?

R. I do.

V. Do you believe in Jesus Christ, his only Son, our Lord, who was born of the Virgin Mary, was crucified, died, and was buried, rose from the dead, and is now seated at the right hand of the Father?

R. I do.

V. Do you believe in the Holy Spirit, the holy Catholic Church, the communion of saints, the forgiveness of sins, the resurrection of the body, and life everlasting?

R. I do.

V. God, the all-powerful Father of our Lord Jesus Christ has given us a new birth by water and the Holy Spirit and forgiven all our sins. May he also keep us faithful to our Lord Jesus Christ for ever and ever.

R. Amen.

Amen. Amen. Amen.

With the goodbyes and thanks out of the way we would drive the short distance back to his house. The curate's house, a new bungalow set off the road on the left just before the entrance to the village. It was about 200 metres from the church beside the national school principal's house. He'd walked ahead of me, opened the door. Invited me in. The door closed behind me. Him or me. I cannot remember.

My head is spinning as I drive over the bridge. I walked across this bridge a thousand times. With Linda first. Then Michael. And Lorna. And

Damien. And alone. I had stood alone on this bridge, in the dark and cold and the wind whipping off the hills and I had cried and I had screamed and I had begged for the pain to go away. I cursed God. I embraced Satan. I lay crumpled. Too strong to die. Too afraid. I stared into the black on dark moonless nights and on frosty nights with the moon full I saw the reflections, heard the water lap gently against the pillars below. I drive off the bridge, past the football field where my father's dreams for me died. Around the Tan Bank and up the small incline towards the curate's house. I was parked and out of my car before I knew where I was. I don't remember ringing the doorbell. I don't remember how I felt.

I remembered him walking down the hall in front of me seventeen years ago. I was eight years old.

Richard Cantwell, P.P., opened the door. He saw me. I stood silently and broken words fell from his mouth: 'I wondered who would be first.'
'Come in.' I followed him into his office on the right. I looked ahead of me, remembering Thomas Naughton's shadow leading me down. His wiry hands swinging by his side.

In his living room he put me sitting on a couch. He sat back in a leather chair. Leaned back in it. Looked at me. Up and down. His right arm fell over the side, rested on a piece of wooden furniture. He turned it around, speaking to me, those eyes fixed on me. I saw cans of Coke and orange stacked neatly.
'If you come sit on my knee, you can have one of these.'
My hands, squashed between my knees, moved. I stood up and walked to him.
Later I would drink my Coke. We would go back to the church. Another christening.
Chrism. Oil. Water. Candles. Rejection of Satan. And all his empty promises. A small brown envelope for the altar boy. A quiet drive back, around the Tan Bank, past the football field. Over the bridge. The swallows darting in and out. As if the wind alone was holding them up. Left and right. Into my driveway. My father's arm raised in salute. His wiry hand on the gear stick. His eyes and his wicked smile the last thing I remember.
'Thank you Father. For looking after him.'

I sit uncomfortably with Richard Cantwell. He is kind. That's my memory of him. He is kind. He tells me he is broken by these revelations. (These are not revelations... how does he only know about this now, or did he know before?). I suspect also by the silence he too has encountered he knows a little of how I feel. It's a strange thing about a small country village. Gossip would spread on the wind like a lit fire through the heather and furze on the hills. Some things, however, seemed to be beyond words. Things involving sex and abuse and rape and boys and a priest. They were things that could never be let take light. I sat silently and listened to what he had to say. He told me he would have to inform the archdiocese. As if they didn't already know. He told me that they would then have to inform the Guards. As if they also didn't already know. He told me that I was brave. He told me that there were many more. He knew of some. As did I.

He knew of others but he didn't think they would come forward. We all knew of others. That night in Valleymount and in the nights to come and the mornings after, mothers sat and looked at quiet men eating dinner, fathers spent late nights in. Men in pubs drank silently and deeply or laughed too much. What else was there to do? What else was there to do? You find a way to survive or you find a way to die. Neither as it happens is a life.

When we had finished speaking he told me I would hear from a liaison officer for the Catholic Church. I often wonder would I have ever heard from the Roman Catholic Church if I hadn't knocked on the door of the house where seventeen years before Tom Naugton had revealed his bribe to an eight-year-old boy and beckoned him to come sit on his knee. I looked right as I walked from his office, down the hallway. He stood at the door as I reversed out and drove away. I'd imagine he was still standing there as I drove back towards the Tan Bank, past the football field, across the bridge, straight past my parents' house where somewhere my father stood in his garden, head bowed and heart beating, the sound of me passing vibrating through him. My mother talking to a friend on the phone.

In time I received a call from the church liaison and then the Guards. I was invited to visit the liaison in his house on Newtownpark Avenue in Blackrock in Dublin. As well as detailing his mandatory responsibility to report my complaint to the Gardai, he brought me into his study and showed me multiple documents relating to Naughton, including a psychiatric report from his time in a treatment centre in Stroud. 'Tom is responding well to treatment but needs constant monitoring.' Weeks later (after this was written) he was back on parish duty in Ringsend with access to children. He talked of 'the occasion of sin' and how the church had made innocent mistakes. 'You'd never put an alcoholic living beside a pub.' At the time I felt seen, I felt vindicated in having come forward. I heard from the Guards, was brought in for questioning, had to provide them with names, dates, details, photographs. The church arranged counselling for me (I didn't really want it at the time). I felt that finally something was happening that might help me. How wrong I was.

Eighteen years later I can look back and see what was happening. I was being groomed, played by the church. This was their playbook. Bring me in, put an arm around me, provide counselling and most importantly show me documents that were hugely incriminating with regard to the conduct and irresponsibility of the hierarchy.

It created an illusion that they were on my side and that I had access to the inside story. I was being played, and it would be a few years, and more, before I fully realised how much.

My next visit to Wicklow to my parents' house was to go through old photograph albums and retrieve photographs of me with Tom Naughton. My communion and my sister's confirmation where Bishop Donal Murray was also present. I took all the images I could find and gave them to the investigating Guards at my next meeting with them. The next time I would see these photographs was when they appeared in an RTE documentary. No one had ever asked me if they could be used. No one ever asked me how their use would make me feel.

The Guards told me they would have to speak with my parents and others in Valleymount. My mother claims she doesn't remember the Guards ever calling to her. I suspect they did. I suspect my parents didn't corroborate my story. Others in Valleymount denied knowing anything. My aunt says the Guards called looking for my parents. The truth lay trapped and silent.

When *Cardinal's Secrets* was televised in 2002 I immediately contacted the reporter Mick Peelo. How had they used my photographs but not spoken to me? He told me that they had called to my parents' house in Valleymount looking to contact me so they could speak with me. My parents took his number and never spoke a word of this visit to me.

In 2000 my best childhood friend died. My mother and his mother were best friends. He was my first friend. I had no brothers and he lived about a mile from my house. We held hands the first day we went to school. We would hold hands many days going into and out of school together. We received our communion together. We became altar boys together. We served Tom Naughton apart. The story I heard from my mother was that he was in the UK and had died from pneumonia. It seemed unbelievable. Unknown to me until recently, my closest childhood friend had succumbed to an addiction. Knowing the reality of his life, of his death, I felt guilt and remorse, anger and sadness. I felt responsible and glad to be alive. I remembered us crouching in the long grass, the matches shaking in our hands as we lit our first Sweet Afton. I remember not liking it but pretending I did because I thought he did. I wonder now, from these years away, I wonder were we both looking to numb the pain and simply found different ways to do it? We drifted apart like the smoke exhaled from our lungs. Our lives didn't intersect much after we were seventeen. By eighteen I had left Valleymount to go to university. We never spoke again. We never saw each other again. I searched his name on the Internet with *Leeds* and *death* and I couldn't find anything. He was my oldest friend and he died with his demons intact. Just because they are numbed doesn't mean they aren't carving you open, inside out.

At his funeral the sun shone as it often seems to do on the bleak hillside of Baltyboys cemetery. I remember crying as his coffin left the church, the lump in my throat not big enough to prevent the tears from sliding down my face. Here we were, together again, in the place where Naughton had wreaked his carnage. My tears were relief that it wasn't me, they were sadness that it was him. I closed my eyes as they walked past me, his mother and father, his brothers and sisters, the incense crawling over my skin like Naughton. I drove slowly behind the hearse, my sunglasses hiding my tears now as we passed the bungalow, the field we hurled together in, the roads we careened around as young boys and teenagers. He didn't have brakes on his bike. He never wanted brakes on his bike.

I stood far back in the graveyard, near where my grandparents were buried. The steep climb to the open grave, the mounds of clay and rock like a small hill. The flowers carried by the hands of his siblings. When he was in the ground and the silence was replaced with at first the gentle murmuring of anguish and shuffling feet they then said a decade of the rosary. For the man in the box in the ground. For the God who didn't save him. I waited alone for the crowd to thin before walking to see his family. I hugged his mum, whispered in her ear that he had been my oldest friend, my first friend. I couldn't speak after that. She asked me to come see her in the weeks and months to come. I never did. The next time I saw her, she was being laid down beside her little boy.

Edward Boyne

was born in the Iveagh flats, Bride Street in the Liberties, inner city Dublin. His father was a shop steward in the Marine Port and General Workers Union and he started the second Credit Union in Ireland. Edward helped out as a volunteer for many years, trying to offer an alternative to the moneylenders. He has published poetry and prose.

Local

The punters. I know where they live. And they know how it is.

I call to their houses, I know their kids' names, I know their kids' birthdays, I know where they drink, who their neighbours are. I make a point of being seen in all the different pubs my punters use. I like to be around, to remind them and to blend in. I'm one of them in a way. Making their repayments should be a friendly act, an extension of neighbourliness. The money is just a side-issue between neighbours, not something we talk about necessarily.

It doesn't matter that I really live somewhere else, in a place they never visit or pass through. It's not that my place is fancy. Nothing like that. I don't go in for ostentation.

The point is that to them I'm someone who is a local. A local is trusted beyond question. Only outsiders aren't trusted. There are obligations towards locals. Paying back a loan on time is one of them. It's all about common sense. No need to get heavy about it.

I don't have a private army of guys with tattoos and over-sized rings on their fingers. No need for that or hardly ever. You see, they know they're going to see me and need me again. Maybe a wedding will crop up or a christening. Some school event for the kids, holy communions, a funeral. Presents have to be bought. Unforeseen expenses. They will need me again so they have to keep me sweet. Like they say on all the best sales courses: it's a relationship. It's for a lifetime.

Things have changed since I started doing this work. People are more grabby. They expect more. There's a lot more competition. Criminals trying to get in on the action. And of course there's the immigrants. They weren't around at all when I started.

Immigrants are a good idea, I don't mind saying. There's more of them visible now. Still a bit of a novelty, but we're getting used to it. We needed a new underclass so we can feel better. That counts for a lot, raises the morale, brings on more spending. It's all about spending. Not about need. That's just do-gooder talk. It's greed not need.

Immigrants are nearly all working on the sly, cleaning houses, minding kids for posh people, so they have cash but no credit credibility. Perfect clients for me. I've told the locals that I charge the immigrants the full rate. Locals get a discount. Goes down well. And it's perfectly true.

It's important to get punters into weekly repayments. That way they have a sense of routine and predictability. And cash loans are not always the best idea. Fuel vouchers in the winter are good, hampers at Christmas work well. They have the feel of gifts. The weekly repayments don't always change, just stretch the loan out, so it feels like an extra, something for free. It's amazing the gratitude I get. Makes the job feel worthwhile.

You could claim that I am exploiting people. Some say that, I'm sure, and they're entitled to their opinion. My way of thinking is straight-forward. They need money. The banks don't want to know. No other lender will look at them. I provide a service. There's a risk. I'm using my own personal money. That means even greater risk. It's my arse on the line. I have to devote myself to the whole business of collection. It's not a neat direct-debit business. Full time devotion, nothing less. Otherwise it doesn't happen. These are the sort of people who'll blow all their dole on one night out drinking then scrounge off each other for the rest of the week. If I didn't ask for a certain amount from them each week on exactly the same day at exactly the same time, they'd spend it all on drink, piss it against the wall. Spend, spend, spend.

Saving with me is a bit of discipline for them.

I've had some difficult punters, no doubt about that. Had a few who disappeared owing me money or went to jail for long stretches. I don't like to chase bad debts from guys just out of jail. You never know who they're mixed up with from their spell inside. They can become ruthless inside. Nothing to lose.

'Have to know when to hold 'em, know when to fold 'em.'

Women with kids make the best punters. They have more of a head for routine. You have to do routine when you have kids. Gotta keep them in line, keep them occupied.

I arrive at their door at the same time every week. Some weeks I do special offers. An extra tenner a week gets you a brand new set of duvets, feather and down. The best. Duvets are very popular in November. I keep the Children's Allowance books sometimes, but I make a point of giving them back, not like some. Like I said, it's all about discipline.

One thing you learn early on is to never talk about the big picture. Keep punters' eyes on the small detail. Make sure the weekly amount is regular and affordable. Let them off a week if they're stuck. They think it's something for nothing. Never mention interest rates or charges. It's something that goes up and down with the banks so why bother yourself about it? Just pay me the same regularly and there'll be no problem. Anyway, I never work out the interest rate I charge. Doubt if it's very much when you take everything into account. Can't keep up with the demand for loans lately, so

I must be doing something right.

Must admit I made the mistake early last year of trying to branch out into a new area, a new housing estate. It was the wife's idea. She knows people who live there and wanted to show off. She thinks I should have staff working for me all over the city. Wants to live over in Las Vegas herself some day. Run the business from over there. Loves America and loves Las Vegas. I can take it or leave it myself but wouldn't tell her that.

'More people have money there and they know how to spend it.'

Only a small bit up the road from the usual old estates but, when I think about it now, definitely 'injun' territory. All kinds of families were dumped there from the inner city. The City Council has a lot to answer for.

The other mistake I made was to ask Sam, her father, to come along as back-up, a bit of security. Looks better if there's more than one person. Nice old guy, bit at a loose end since he retired. He thinks I'm working for some finance company that collects door to door. Strictly speaking that's no lie.

He was a boxer once when he was in the army. Makes out still like he's fearless, but he probably couldn't knock a hen off a stool. He once helped start a Credit Union in his own area back in the day, so he picked up a bit of knowledge about loans and the like. Not that we talk much about that. Credit Unions are not really my thing unless I fancy a car loan for myself. Don't go in for all that community stuff. Not good for business.

Everything went fine at the new place for the first few weeks. We drove up early on Tuesdays and Thursdays and parked near the bookies shop beside the shopping centre, nice and discreet down a side-lane. The father-in-law stayed in the car reading the paper. I did my usual routine of letting people know I'm around. Got a few starter intros from the wife and they introduced their friends and so on. The bookies shop is always the best place to start. People will talk to you there, they'll meet you there. It's all about easy money in that shop. It's all about the 'now'.

I love 'now' people. Can't get enough of 'now' people. 'Tomorrow' to them is unreal, and then it arrives and it's just another form of 'now'.

I never part with cash out on the street. Have to go to the punter's own home to establish what I need to establish. I have to know about their kids, their ages, where they go to school. Need to know the names of their neighbours, I make a point of writing all this down in front of them. Makes them behave. Then I make them wait until the following week for the cash. Decorum and protocol. Bit of ritual.

It doesn't matter about other loans they might have. I can roll them all up into a single weekly payment. No problem.

It was raining slightly early on the third Tuesday and we were sitting in the car drinking from a flask of coffee the father-in-law brought.

I had cash with me for half a dozen loans that had all been arranged the week before and a number of appointments planned. It was all starting to feel like hard work, like having to start over. A bit unnecessary. I was thinking of ways to hand it on to someone else.

I heard the left rear door open, then the right rear door and two men sat in behind us cool as you like. Said: 'Good morning.'

I turned my head around said: 'Sorry lads this isn't a taxi.' They were both wearing scarves up over their noses.

One of them had a long knife with a serrated blade. He was cleaning his thumb-nail with it.

'I wouldn't turn around again if I were you,' the knife-man said. 'Could be unhealthy.'

The voice sounded helpful. It also sounded strangely familiar, but I knew not to go there and that it wasn't a joke.

I wasn't afraid, although maybe I should have been. I knew by his friendly tone that he only wanted the money and no fuss.

I was just nervous that Sam would try something heroic. I said: 'I have what you want here lads,' trying to make it sound like everything was normal. I put a hand on Sam's knee to reassure him and keep him quiet. He was shaking.

'That will be fine,' knife-man said. 'I hope the rain clears off soon.'

I took the cash envelopes from my briefcase and passed them back to him without looking.

'It's all there,' I said.

'I'm sure it is. I'm afraid I can't give you a receipt today. I'll post it on.'

He had the car door open when he said 'Our special offer this week. One little going-over for the price of two. We won't look for your wallet this time Sam. We understand you're just on the pension but we know where you live if you decide to squeal. That goes for your genius son-in-law here as well. Only this one week mind. Business as usual next week, so cheerio.'

We revved it out of there as fast as we could. We agreed not to tell anyone, including the wife.

No telling what might happen. The idea might catch on in other places.

The wife and I didn't hear from Sam for a good while after. I heard he wasn't all that well. She didn't suspect anything.

I'm going to keep it low-key now and deal only with people I know and trust. Business is good. The recession was a great help, just as demand was starting to slacken off. No plans to branch out again in the near future and Las Vegas will always be there.

The wife is still on at me about it. Wants to buy an apartment there. Told her I'm working on expansion plans and I'll get back to her.

You know how it is.

Bern Butler

is an Irish writer and educator. She grew up in Shantalla, Galway, in one of the city's first-built council estates, number seven in a family of eight children. She would love to live in Shantalla again, but cannot afford to despite having bettered herself through education. She works full-time in Adult Education and spent 24 years working in prison education.

Her writing has featured in *Force 10*, *The Grey Castle*, *Ropes Anthology*, *The Galway Review*, *Vox Galvia*, *North West Words*, *The Blue Nib*, *Pendemic.ie* and *Abridged 0-60*. She holds an MA in Writing (NUIG), has been a featured reader in Galway City Library's *Over the Edge* Library Readings.

A Tale of Two Cities 1985
(i.m. of my father and mother)

It was the worst of times.

By the tall window of the tearoom in a recruitment agency on a London high street in July 1985 Tracy, a secretarial assistant, was regaling her boss Sandra with the story of the young woman who'd come into the agency that morning.

'She was talking about a druid,' Tracy said, 'as if that should mean something to me. She was pointing to the card we'd placed in the window about vacancies in theatre. I asked her if she was trained but she started talking about the druid again. Said she did a summer in druid.' Tracy made air quotes and looked at Sandra, who was smoking and staring out the window, appearing transfixed by the lilac bush growing out of the wall below.

'I asked her where this druid was. She said *Galway*. I said I had never heard of Galway. *Is it somewhere in Ireland?* She said, *It's straight across from Dublin on the other side.* Have you heard of it?'

Sandra, now examining her nail polish, replied, 'There's a famous golf course there right on the seafront.' She extended her hand away from herself to get a better view of her nails. 'It crosses the main road apparently. Marcus went with the club last year.' With the other hand she took a drag of her cigarette.

'She said she had done *front of house* the previous summer. Was willing to try anything!' Tracy interrupted her own narrative with a chuckle of further realisation. 'Then I suddenly got it.' She joshed against Sandra's arm. 'She thought we were looking for people to work in the West End! In the theatre! Ha ha! The poor thing wasn't any kind of nurse.'

Sandra squashed her cigarette into the bottom of her water cup where it hissed and went out. She crushed the cup and tossed it into the bin 'How very Irish,' she said, walking away.

***

It was hot in the city and sunlight seared and bounced off everything, blinding me. All I could picture as I made my way back to the bus stop was the image of the po-faced woman in the agency; mouth twitching behind her hand, mirth silently shaking her shoulders, her condescending English accent calling me *luv*.

We're not that kind of agency, luv.

On the bus I kicked myself; apologised silently to all the Irish people living in London for having further entrenched the notion of the thick Irish Paddy. Five stops into the journey I got off the bus again, having realised that while I was on the right bus, it was going the wrong way.

Story of my life.

I had borrowed £100 from my father back in Galway to help see me through the first couple of weeks of my summer in London. I was a student. It was all the money I had, and it was running out. I was worried about not finding work and becoming a burden on my older sister who was putting me up. I was also worried about the possibility of not being able to pay my father back. This concern loomed larger than it might normally have done because my father, who had worked for decades as a fitter in Galway Regional Hospital, was on strike.

The strike arose out of an incident when one of my father's colleagues (reputedly) in an argument with a foreman, punched him. My father was also a foreman but not long promoted to that position. The man who threw the punch was quickly fired and his colleagues went out on strike in support of what they saw as unfair dismissal. My father, taking a stance against the management he had just joined, went out on strike with his colleagues. What I recall feeling at the time is youthful, naïve admiration because my father was supporting the underdog, sticking to his principles, and putting himself on the line; he was a hero in my eyes. This made the business then of paying my father back a matter of principle *for me*. I was desperately keen to show that I could repay the money and honour the trust my father placed in me by lending it, especially under the dire circumstances. At the time of the strike, four of my seven siblings (including myself ordinarily) were still living at home: only one working.

Certainly not the best of times.

On the suggestion of my sister in London I went looking for work in Pond's, the makers of Vaseline, skin lotions and a host of other cosmetics. My sister had heard they took on people for the summer and the money was reasonable.

So, I did an interview and hey-ho, I got a job.

The Pond's factory was located on the Victoria Road in N.W. London in a huge red-brick building, looking like it was built during the industrial revolution. Inside was a vast space made up of adjoining sheds with brickwork painted white. The ceiling was high as a cathedral; instead of pillars there were criss-crossed metal structures like arms of cranes or electricity pylons. The air rang with the sound of whirring machines, with bottles and jars, both plastic and glass, clinking and rattling as they bobbed in thousands along assembly lines stretching the length of the building. Each assembly line was *manned* at junctures by workers (mostly women) placing empty vessels on the conveyor belt, or further along, capping, labelling, testing, or packing the finished product.

They put me on the cocoa-butter line. Another Irish woman trained me in. My job was to stock the moving conveyor belt with empty plastic containers. Opposite the workstation at which we stood, an arm's reach across the conveyor belt, sat a huge vat of empty cream-coloured bottles with a small section cut-out at the bottom of the vat. The job was to reach across, pick up the bottles, and once the conveyor belt had started, place them on the belt without leaving any gaps. This meant your hands had to move like the clappers! In addition, when you had caught up with yourself and could see the vat was emptying, you had to run around to the back of it, rip open a giant-sized new bag of bottles (or more if you were quick enough) and fill up the vat, then run back around to the conveyor belt, picking up where you'd left off.

Woe betide you if you left any gaps! The bottles had to line-up neatly one after the other. If there was a space left, the pre-programmed machine at the next juncture, would squirt out the cocoa-butter anyway. If this happened the line mechanic came running, shaking his fists and cursing you for having put a stop to the whole operation. Then he and everyone else stood, arms folded, watching while you mopped up the mess and righted the bottles.

That first day, I watched the Irish woman's hands work in a blur: she was cartoon-fast! She'd been working in Pond's for several years. Her movements were focused and precise, her concentration never wavered even though sometimes she exchanged conversations with a colleague on another line, or spoke with a supervisor holding a clipboard, who had come to check something with her. She, the entire factory floor workforce, and now me too worked in this manner for several hours at a stretch. We could only stop if the line's operation buckled or when the klaxon sounded for tea or lunch break.

In the meantime I had received a letter from my sister in Galway telling me I had passed my exams in university, which meant I could go on to do my Higher Diploma and hopefully qualify as a teacher. This was big news in a working-class neighbourhood like mine. Likewise for my family.

I was relieved to have passed my exams; I had found university challenging and had felt oppressed by its middle-class mores, which focused on qualification rather than education and exploration. However, I must admit to feeling glad I was not going to be working in Pond's factory for very long, or in another place like it somewhere else. In Pond's what I did gain was first-hand experience of factory work on a grand scale and an appreciation, which has never left me, of the skill, diligence, not to mention the ability to cope with the sheer drudgery that *actual* hard work entails.

Thirty years later, I still possess about twenty letters my family back in Galway sent to me that summer in London. One of them, dated 15th of July, begins:

> *We were delighted you got your exams and I hope you enjoyed celebrating on Saturday night.*

It is from my father, who proceeds to write of everyday life in the Butler household, and packs a diverse selection of news into two single-sided blue pages. He wrote in an unselfconscious, straightforward style I loved. The fact he wrote at all was something of a marvel, considering he left school aged eleven or so, and being more often absent than present in the classroom prior to that.

He wasn't, Dad would admit himself, *much of a scholar* and while there is evidence of that (his letters are speckled with spelling errors) he was highly skilled and creatively gifted in everything he decided to pursue: in his work, his furniture making, woodturning, gardening, tree-planting, boat building, in his singing and accordion playing, poetry writing, in his knowledge and observations of the natural world.

Much of his letter of the 15th is taken up with fruit: blackcurrants, raspberries and strawberries himself and my mother were harvesting from the allotment they kept on the outskirts of Galway city, how my mother made jam, and my sister froze pounds of blackcurrants. Also selecting to share the detail of my five-year-old nephew insisting on picking the *red* blackcurrants too *because he liked the colours.*

My father includes a hilarious picture of how our dog is reacting to the cat my sister brought back from Dublin. He says the dog imposed strict sentry duty on himself in the back garden and if the cat appeared, would observe her closely until she settled somewhere unawares, then sneak up behind her and chase her onto the roof of the shed. I loved how my father would write about such things, which a lot of adults would consider childish or unimportant. He was so interested in everything.

Next included is a very precise sharing of how the central heating and rewiring of the house is going. (He would have grabbed the opportunity to take on these jobs because he was home from work.) He tells me he is assisted by my two brothers, is putting in another socket beside my bed and ruminates over what to do with a floor-to-ceiling triangular cupboard in one corner, and decides he will put some shelves in there, telling me *it would look nice*. A line which communicated love so palpably it made me cry.

There is news of two babies born in that same letter, of my London nephew being *a busy little fellow*, of a friend winning a music competition in Salthill, of the friend giving our dog a lift home because my parents had gone unusually to play slot machines and the dog got bored!

Finally, he tells me he is *relieved I got a nice job.*

I guess I must have lied.

There is no mention of the strike which was ongoing. No complaint, but no news of resolution either. Then his letter ends, in response to an invitation in my previous letter to him, with a request:

> '*You were asking if I wanted something for the workshop. Well I would like a new drill with a Hammer action Black and Decker 1/2". They are much cheaper over there.*'

A month later, shortly before I pack to go home, my sister and I go to Argos to buy the drill. There would have been no Argos in Ireland then. I find the exact one my father is looking for. Back in my sister's flat I fill my haversack with my bounty, thank my sister and young nephew, bid them adieu and head back to resume life in that city *directly across from Dublin on the other side!*

By the time I get home, my father's work situation has resolved itself; the man who'd been dismissed had gotten his job back, my father was back at work, our household back on track. I felt proud handing over the drill and giving back the money I had borrowed. It was as if I had passed an initiation into adulthood. I felt that on the brink of my working life, I was lucky to have had a father and mother, who had demonstrated that sometimes it is necessary to act consciously and independently, that on such an occasion it is best to act according to your instinct, be that popular or not; that is, not to follow power slavishly as a lot of people do, as daisies follow sun.

Sinéad Cameron

was born in Belfast. Her father was the first person from his working-class family to go to university as a mature student after saving enough money working on the building site to support his studies. He now works as a secondary school teacher and proudly considers himself working class.

Sinéad graduated from Queens University Belfast in the summer of 2019 with a Masters in Architecture. Since then, she has been juggling working a minimum wage job while trying to get a foot into the creative industry, by volunteering, taking on design commissions and occasionally selling work. She has a keen interest in exploring the boundaries between art and architecture. In October 2019 she exhibited her sculptural work as part of a group exhibition in Platform Arts Belfast.

Worker Dispenser

Brian Campfield

was born and raised on Belfast's working-class Falls Road area. He worked for the Northern Ireland Housing Executive in the late 1970s, mainly in housing redevelopment areas such as Short Strand and Falls Road, before becoming a full-time trade union official with the Northern Ireland Public Service Alliance. From the early 1980s to 2007 he was at various times the secretary and President of Belfast Trades Union Council. He is a former President of the Irish Congress of Trade Unions. He was also a member of the Belfast Executive of the Northern Ireland Civil Rights Association, a member of the Official Republican Movement in the early 1970s, and from 1975 he has been a member of the Communist Party of Ireland.

O'Donnell Holds Court

They came in their hundreds to the Conway Mill on Belfast's Falls Road, on that Saturday afternoon, in April 1984, to listen to the legend Peadar O'Donnell, the writer and left-wing political activist, who despite his ninety plus years, was as lucid as ever and just as committed to the cause of both Labour and Ireland. The occasion was organised to mark the 50th anniversary of the founding of the Republican Congress, a bold but unsuccessful attempt to rally the workers and small farmers for social and economic emancipation: 'Break the Connection with Capitalism' was the slogan emblazoned on the banner carried by Belfast's Shankill Road contingent at the Wolfe Tone commemoration in Bodenstown in 1934.

A political 'Galway Races', where the multitudes assembled, and in attendance, yes, there were indeed Catholics and Protestants, Jews and Presbyterians, a few Quakers and socialists of virtually every persuasion. Officials and Provisionals, the array of different Trotskyists, trade unionists as well as locals, all wanted to hear speak the man with a connection to the Irish war of independence, the Civil War, the man who prevented Glenveagh Castle in Donegal from being burnt to the ground, the comrade of Mellows, Barrett, McKelvey and O'Connor who were executed by the Free State government.

In an electrifying atmosphere in the old mill, various groups of people milled around, no overt animosity, just the grudging acknowledgement of political opponents, the bitterness of various splits and schisms, personal and political animosities being put on hold, for a few hours at least. Like the Republican Congress, most of those in the hall would have experienced the divisions that were all too common in Labour, Republican and Left politics in Ireland. It was another Irish writer and political activist, Brendan Behan, who made the quip that the first item on the agenda of any new political organisation in Ireland was 'the split', such was the almost pathological mentality of the Irish Left to elevate those issues that divided rather than

29

united them. But then, the Irish Left have no more claim to this dubious honour than their counterparts in other countries.

But on this occasion, at least, there seemed to exist tacit acceptance that O'Donnell was a participant in much of that shared history. It helped also that the meeting was to be chaired by Sean Morrissey, former republican internee in the 1940s, Communist Party Executive member, secretary of Turf Lodge Tenants' Association and General Executive member of the Amalgamated Transport and General Workers' Union. The other speaker was Eoin O'Murchu, author of the Official Republican Repsol pamphlet *Culture and the Revolution*, and later to become the political correspondent for Raidió na Gaeltachta.

O'Donnell didn't disappoint. Always opposed to the negative influence of the Catholic Church in Irish political life, he told the story of the flying column in West Cork, during the war of independence. Holding up a crucifix, a priest confronted the column warning them that they had to choose between Christ or Moylan. He was of course referring to Sean Moylan, the guerrilla leader, who features in that great ballad 'The Galtee Mountain Boy'. After a moment's deliberation, the leader of the column made their position clear, 'By Christ, it's Moylan', using the name of Christ to justify the choice, reinforcing the disregard among republicans for church interference, in what was to them, a secular struggle for democracy and independence.

O'Donnell was an internationalist, heavily involved in organising support for the democratically elected Spanish Republic against the forces of General Franco and his fascist Italian and Nazi German allies. A few years earlier, in 1930 in Berlin, he formally opened the European Congress of Peasants and Working Farmers and told the story of how he was approached by some 'shadowy' figures and asked to chair the conference on the basis that progressives in every country respected Ireland's long history of agrarian struggle. Not being naïve he retorted 'Oh! I see, you want me to be the green dickie that hides your red shirt,' and promptly agreed to the invitation. The same year a Working Farmers' Conference in Galway condemned the payment of Land Annuities to Britain and at the meeting in the Mill, O'Donnell explained the campaign of refusal to pay the land annuities and the strategy of forcing Fianna Fail to support the abolition of the land annuities payments —which duly happened some years after Fianna Fail won the elections in 1932 and subsequent years. The organisers of the Berlin Conference weren't bad judges at all.

There was no shyness from the audience during the subsequent debate and discussion; the political advances achieved in the North since 1970 were the result of the 'cutting edge of the IRA'; 'O'Donnell was culpable along with Stalin in the death of Trotsky'. While O'Donnell's speech that day was recorded on video and is available from the Communist Party, the ensuing debate doesn't appear to be have been recorded. April 1984 wasn't a quiet time on the streets. The backdrop to the meeting in the Mill was one of violence. Gerry Adams had been shot and injured the previous week.

O'Donnell chuckled as he narrated anecdote after anecdote, enjoying the atmosphere and the cut and thrust of the debate, virtually impregnable as he responded to observation and criticism alike. The meeting concluded, those present were thanked for their attendance and the audience dispersed peaceably. It was at a social gathering later that evening in the CP premises in Exchange Place in Belfast City Centre that O'Donnell chatted with the likes of Joe Deighan and Albert Fry, both leading figures in Cumann Chluain Árd at different times. Albert had been the guest speaker at a meeting organised by the West Belfast Branch of the Communist Party a few years earlier in the Lake Glen Hotel, on the Andersonstown Road. 'Culture and the Revolution' was the theme of that meeting which was conducted mainly in the Irish Language. Joe Deighan chaired that meeting. Joe was an associate of C Desmond Greaves, biographer of James Connolly and Liam Mellows in the Connolly Association, an offshoot of the Republican Congress in England, which to this day endures as the foremost organisation for Irish workers in Britain. Unlike, of course, the Lake Glen hotel, which was destroyed in a bomb attack in 1983.

Albert Fry lived a stone's throw from the hotel, and still does—well, the site, which is now a Bingo Hall—and as I scribble together this short piece, the Raidió na Gaeltachta programme 'Barrscéalta' reminds listeners that Albert celebrated his 80th birthday on Monday 25th May. Albert and Peadar conversed about The Rosses, Donegal, and about another great Irish writer Seosamh Mac Grianna, from Rannafast, in the Donegal Gaeltacht, an area well known to both. It was Mac Grianna who translated a number of Peadar's novels into Irish, and Albert would have been a friend of the Mac Grianna clann, not least his neighbour Mairtin Mc Grianna, fellow activist in Cumann Chluain Árd.

Enough of the streams of consciousness, association of ideas, digressions and diversions; such a journey down the byways instead of the highways would unearth many an interesting tale and a hidden history. Therein lies another project. Interestingly enough, in the 1970s, 'The Internationale' would sometimes be played on a Friday night by the traditional musicians in the Cumann Chluain Árd, under a poster of Máirtín Ó Cadhain ('Sí an Ghaeilge athghabháil na hÉireann agus is í athghabháil na hÉireann slánú na Gaeilge') and on one occasion a priest from the local St. Paul's Parish, from the altar, as was their custom, warned the faithful about the potential dangers to their souls if they frequented such a place. Like the Flying Column in Cork, the priest's 'advice' was ignored.

No stuffed shirts, snobbery or superiority complexes. No saviour from on high was expected to deliver, either in the context of workers' emancipation or the Irish Language; just the unstinting and unselfish energy and efforts of comrades and activists, anti-sectarian, anti-imperialist, internationalist, struggling not just to decolonise society and the economy but the very mind itself. Many of their stories have still to be told.

Michael G. Casey

was brought up in New Ross and went to the local Christian Brothers' School. His formal training is in economics. He has written about the need to curb the excesses of the financial sector by means of Tobin taxes and proper regulation, and the tendency for government and the legal system to privilege the wealthy. In his book, Ireland's Malaise, he proposes the Share Economy as the most appropriate industrial structure for Ireland.

Fadings

After her second cup of tea Cynthia O'Reilly gave her husband a peck on the cheek and went out to her car. To her amazement it was covered in thick reddish-brown stains like small over-cooked pancakes. She stood for a long time trying to figure out what might have happened. Tentatively, using an index finger, she was relieved to find that the splodges came off and that her lunar green metallic paintwork would not be damaged. She held the finger to her nose but there was no discernible smell.

She noticed the same rash of stains on the concrete driveway and —across the hedge—on her neighbour's car. What on earth had happened? God forbid it was airborne waste from Sellafield? The sense of puzzlement contained more than a seed of anxiety. She looked up at the sky, which seemed perfectly normal for a spring morning; indeed, she heard skylarks singing.

On the way to work she observed that most of the traffic was mottled with the same sort of red-brown lichens. Other drivers seemed equally puzzled. At a set of traffic lights on the Merrion Road she wound down the window and asked her neighbouring road-user if she had any explanation.

'I've no idea,' she said with an apologetic shrug. 'It's extraordinary... Maybe it's something to do with aliens?' she added unhelpfully before revving up when the lights changed.

When Cynthia was young, a morbilliform rash had appeared on her body one morning. The doctor put it down to teenage angst and didn't prescribe anything; a few days later the tiny lesions had all disappeared. Could an entire city or country develop a rash? What the hell was going on?

When she got to the lobby of her office building the receptionist greeted her with a smile which seemed a little more restrained than usual. Cynthia was on the point of asking her about the extraordinary epidemic of liver spots when she cut in,

'Isn't it awful about Jack?' With barely a pause she went on, 'He died in his sleep on Saturday morning. His remains have gone to the church already.'

'Jack?' Cynthia repeated.

'And he seemed fine on Friday. Worked his full shift on the shop floor. Was in great form apparently. It's a terrible shock for all of us.'

'It certainly is,' Cynthia mumbled. 'Awful.' She stepped into the elevator. She knew most of the staff who worked on the floor, at least to see, but she wasn't good with names. Which one was Jack? Which one had been Jack?

On the fifth floor a woman from Personnel got in.

'Sad news.' She looked dolefully down at her shoes.

'Terrible.'

'He was so full of life...always smiling...'

Cynthia nodded.

'And he loved practical jokes.'

'Yes.' She decided to take a risk. 'And at such a ...young age ...'

'Well, he wasn't all that young.' The woman looked curiously at her.

'No. But nowadays...you know. The floor won't be the same.'

'No. It certainly won't.'

When she got to her desk she took the newspaper from her briefcase and turned to the obituary page. But she realised immediately that she didn't have the surname. Then it occurred to her that the surname might not mean anything to her either.

She tried to get on with her work, but the matter kept niggling at her. Faces of colleagues swam into her consciousness. Which one was Jack's face? She must have known him to see. Several faces came to her, but she was almost certain that Jack's face wasn't among them.

She was relieved when the Production Manager stuck his head around the door.

'Come in, Tom. Pull up a pew.'

After a sympathetic exchange about Jack they turned to business.

'One of the lines is down,' Tom said.

'Maintenance...?'

'Yeah, they're looking at it. They reckon we won't be back to full production until tomorrow afternoon.' Tom wore a long-suffering expression. 'They just love to milk these situations.'

'Well, inventories aren't too bad at the moment,' Cynthia said. 'But don't tell them that. Maybe we could fit in an extra shift later in the week to catch up?'

'It's possible, I suppose.'

She changed tack. 'Listen...about Jack...'

'We're all devastated...'

She decided to come clean. She could confide in Tom. 'I'm drawing a blank. I'm sure I knew him.... but right now for some reason.... I just can't place him ....' She leant forward across the desk, aware of the fact that her voice had dropped to a lower, almost conspiratorial, register.

'Jack Cremmins. You know...the live wire. Reddish hair, average height...He nearly always wore those faded jeans...'

'Oh, and a moustache?'

'No. Clean-shaven. He had a sort of ruddy complexion.'

'A bit overweight? Cynthia raised her eyebrows in hopeful anticipation.

'Thin as a lath.'

'Jesus, I just can't place him, Tom. Don't tell anyone for God's sake.'

Tom told her not to worry about it. As he was leaving the office, he said he'd probably see her later at the funeral.

'Oh...yes. The funeral....' Cynthia quickly scanned her diary. She would have to attend. After Tom left she looked up the Cremmin's funeral notice. Mass at eleven, then the cemetery. The usual drill. But there wasn't much time.

She rang Personnel, then went down to the shop floor, ostensibly to have a word with the foreman who said that if a line had to go down, now was as good a time as any. Because of Jack's death no one was at the top of their form. Cynthia noticed several workers standing around chatting, not even making a pretence of work despite the presence of the foreman and herself.

'Remind me where Jack worked,' Cynthia said.

The foreman pointed towards the end of the line, just in front of the packaging section.

'Oh yes, quality control,' Cynthia dissembled, feeling such a fraud. A young girl in white overalls stood there now, just in front of the framed colour print of a model pizza, against which the pizzas that travelled along the conveyor belt were to be judged. Cynthia couldn't help noticing that she junked about one in eight. She wondered if Jack had been so meticulous or whether she was overdoing it. For the life of her she could not summon up a picture of the man who had stood in that spot for fifteen odd years, junking sub-standard pizzas. She had a sudden vision of a face which might have been the one, but it evaporated as quickly as it had come, and, try as she might, she could not call it back. Why was it so important to her? If she couldn't recall the face, then she couldn't remember the person, and then she couldn't grieve properly. Was that it? Or maybe she would be haunted for years and then wake up one morning and be confronted by the face of the ghost, when she least expected it. Was that it, some loss of power or of closure? Or maybe it was simply a question of respect.

She let her eyes wander all over the floor, looking at the men and women in their white overalls and caps. She hoped that, by some process of elimination, she might be able to establish Jack's identity. She knew almost all of the faces, but which one was missing? She began to realise how difficult it was to perceive absence. She felt bad. A man had stood at that spot for fifteen years doing a menial job, had somehow managed to keep his spirits up, as well as those of his co-workers, and she, Cynthia, could not recall who he was. And she had always prided herself on being a good people-person.

Jack's personal file was on her desk when she got back. It contained a brief CV, a couple of references from previous employers, and an attendance record. There was also a copy of a memo reprimanding him for a practical joke which had backfired, resulting in the loss of an hour's production. A fake rat had apparently so shocked one of the ladies in the pie-crust section that she had to be sent home in a taxi. Cynthia closed the file. There was no photograph.

At the funeral mass, she went to the front of the church. The coffin was closed. She knelt in the pew behind the family members. She had certainly never met the widow, not even at Christmas parties. There were two middle-aged men with reddish hair, probably Jack's brothers. Both of them did readings from the altar. She studied their faces minutely as they read, but they didn't put her in mind of anyone in particular. She found herself staring at the coffin, wondering who exactly lay inside the highly polished oak.

She tried to put his face together, feature by feature, nose, eyes, mouth. But no combination fused into a recognisable whole. Maybe there were no distinguishing features as such. She tried a gestalt, top-down approach, an overall impression of the facial expression, but that didn't work either.

In the funeral procession to the cemetery she noticed how most of the cars were marked by that strange brown substance. The hearse was an obvious exception; it had probably been washed earlier that morning.

At they stood around the open grave Cynthia felt a stirring of memory. A blurred face began to rise up before her. When the mourners threw fistfuls of clay into the grave, they landed on the coffin lid like the red-brown marks she had seen that morning. The strange similarity banished the facial image from her mind.

Afterwards, Cynthia offered her condolences to the widow and explained who she was.

'Jack mentioned you often,' the widow said. Although her face was tear-stained she was quite controlled, even to the point of putting other people at their ease. 'He liked you.'

'Me too,' Cynthia said, miserably. 'We were all very fond of Jack.' She felt such a hypocrite. She hoped she would invite her back to the house. There would be family photographs, other memorabilia...But she didn't get an invitation, and she couldn't very well just turn up on the doorstep.

That evening, stuck in traffic, she noticed that the cars and trucks were cleaner than they had been that morning. Many had obviously been washed during the day or the stains had just faded away. Others, including her own, had had the benefit of an April shower at about 5.30 p.m. The rain had at least blurred the splodges which, she learned from the car radio, had been caused by a combination of freak winds and a sandstorm in the Sahara.

The other mystery was likely to haunt her forever.

Gráinne Daly

lives in Tallaght, Dublin. Educated at Firhouse Community College, she worked in a local chipper and subsequently Dunnes Stores to fund her way through college and enable her to undertake a number of postgraduate courses. After many years of working as a personal assistant, when her role was made redundant a couple of years ago she viewed it as an opportunity to focus on her life's passion: writing. Currently pursuing a PhD in Creative Writing, she is a Creative Writing tutor at University College Dublin and volunteers as a learning assistant in the Museum of Literature, Ireland. Sport in creative literature is her primary research interest.

The Dublin-Meath Saga

It may have been Kevin Foley's late goal or Jinksy Beggy's point that ruined what was left of my childhood. After fourteen halves of football, decades upon decades of the rosary and an unhealthy amount of excitement, by any human standards, the saga of the summer was settled on the fourth time of asking, when Dublin met Meath in Croke Park in July 1991.

The preliminary round of the Leinster football championship had been a draw, the replay a further draw, the replay of the replayed game was to have the same fate—a draw after extra time—so it's not surprising that by the fourth game, the battle had the attention of every man, woman and child in the land. My brother and I were two of those children, I was ten years of age and he five. We had grown up in Kingscourt, County Cavan, but by some kink of feckituppery our dad had gone and blown the marriage, so we had been hauled to Tallaght to live with our nanny, our house sold to clear the debts, and with nothing more than two redhaired kids and a silver Datsun Cherry she'd bought for a few bob that she borrowed off her sister, it was back home to Dublin for Mam and us. The car was her first one to own. It had an orange stripe running along the side and crumbled to scabs of rust in your hands, but it was Mam's car and we loved it.

The first game came around, and seeing as I had grown up close to the Cavan-Meath border I knew the Meath team inside out. On my bedroom wall I had a centrefold of a match programme of the Meath team as well as Dublin. Not because I liked the Royals, might I add, but what's that saying about keeping your friends close...? When Meath had won the All Ireland in '88, the Sam Maguire, full of sweets, was brought into our school PE hall in Kingscourt by Brian Stafford, who you could almost call a local man. He was from just up the road in Kilmainhamwood, and was one of the very rare breed of Meath players I can say I ever liked. My mam used to cut his hair so maybe I was biased. I remember the morning well, the hall filled with eager Cavan kids being shown the cup by a Meath man; a strange state of affairs for most of the assembly, with the exception of the few who lived the dark side of the Meath

38

border. 'Up Cyaaaaavan' roared one of the McKennas after he had taken a fistful of sweets from the cup, 'up the Ryls' replied the Meath crew.

On the 2nd of June there was the usual fever pitch you used to get whenever the pair would meet. Back then Meath were good, and since Dublin hadn't been in winning mode since the 80s, there was added hunger. My Mam had to work that day; she had returned to a job she'd had in her teens in the Macari take-away in Tallaght village. Sometimes she would do a few nights in Borza's too. It paid the bills although there wasn't enough for me to ask her for a Dublin jersey. Arnotts had taken over the sponsorship and jerseys were just becoming a thing, taking over from the rosettes and the soft cardboard caps. Everyone had them; my cousins left Tallaght that morning to head to the match in their new blue Arnotts jerseys. I would have loved one but there was simply no money. By that stage we had been in Dublin a year and Dad had recently got back in touch with Mam (to let us know he was still alive and to inquire about meeting us). I knew he'd be watching that game. I guess I wished I could be watching it with him, like old times. Things were looking good for Dublin until Colm Coyle ruined any chances of a Dublin victory. Mam brought home leftover Southern Fried Chicken and we ate it in the kitchen after midnight. She told me that Dublin would do it the next day. I believed her.

By the time the next day came, which was the 9th of June, a soft and dirty old day in Dublin, Dad had been in touch again and talks of the pair reconciling had progressed. Of course, aside from wanting a Dublin jersey, I wanted a normal family; all my cousins' mothers and fathers were together, and none of them were poor, so I didn't want to be an anomaly. To tell the truth, I had been praying for them to get back together ever since he had walked out. I prayed and I prayed and I prayed. That I wanted Dublin to win was unquestionable, but wanting Dad back was the sum total of everything. Mam decided to meet up with him and we would go for a drive on the Sunday. Of course, we would have the match on in the car. So, in the pouring rain on a slate grey Sunday we found ourselves up on the Military Road pulled in by Lemass's Cross. Barney Rock was in blistering form and was bringing the game to Meath. My least favourite player, Mick Lyons, saw red. A draw meant it went to extra time. Dad was sitting in the passenger seat, both him and Mam in good form, my brother beside me chewing sweets, smiling every time Dublin scored, pinching me when Meath did. As days go, it was turning out to be a good one. Sheet rain poured across the windscreen; a mountain breeze shook the Datsun Cherry and the four of us in it; Tommy Howard got a cramp in Croke Park but got seen to and continued to referee what seemed to be Dublin's game. Dad stretched across and held Mam's hand; she smiled and said something that sounded like 'typical trucking Meath you can never rule them out.' It was nearing the end of the game and my brother was out of sweets so he decided to pinch no matter who scored; I sat there, hands in full-on prayer mode, imploring God in the month of the Sacred Heart to help Dublin win. David Beggy put Meath ahead, Jack Sheedy equalised, Tommy Howard found the whistle.

Whatever it is they say about third time being lucky I don't buy. The third game (second replay) took place on the 23rd of June. Mam was again in work, so I watched it with my nanny. I can't remember where my brother was for the day, gone off fishing with my uncle probably, but I recall that Mam had left me a pound for if I wanted to go to the shops to get some foosies for the game. What I wanted was to be at the game, preferably in a jersey of my own, with Dad by my side. Nanny had never been a cursing woman, even a few years before when she had watched her own son, my uncle, play for Dublin, but that day was an exception. The inspiration for her language was Bernard Flynn's extra time goal that choked Dublin's lead. She was also ticked off with Brian Stafford's points that sealed the deal and drew it level for the Royals. Suffice to say, there were a few rounds of the Angelus said in Nanny's cottage in Old Court that evening. I knew what Dad would say: 'Oh well, that's sport,' which I was grateful I didn't have to hear in the aftermath of another nail-biter, but I still prayed that night that maybe by the next game my parents would be back together.

The sun came out in all its splendour for the fourth game on the 6th of July. Lo and behold, Dad had been in touch with Mam and decided we would watch the match together, only there wasn't really anywhere to watch a match given he was living in a shoebox bedsit in Terenure with a portable black and white telly, and Nanny didn't allow us have any visitors (and by that stage, hated Dad anyway). The GAA club was too local and would only fuel rumours of a 'they're back together' nature, which I would have been more than proud with, Mam's family less so. It being a Saturday, and the first time the GAA were to televise a Saturday game, Mam thought that the pubs would be too busy. Truth is, she hadn't a washer to her name and didn't want to let him know that. The decision was made to listen to it in the car on another drive up the mountains. We went out towards the Glencree Centre, ironically now a centre for reconciliation, then up to Kippure only to discover that the radio in the car wouldn't tune in properly that far up, so back towards Glencree we came. Reception clear as day. A purple blush of heather stretched up the shoulder of the hill beside us. The valley before us ablaze with furze. My brother chewed through a penny mix. There was no pinching this time as the four of us sat in relative silence save for the odd breakout of 'come on the Dubs'. There was no handholding in the front. Keith Barr missed a penalty for Dublin and I kicked the back of the seat only to get an earful from Mam. Then, in a case of excruciating familiarity, it ended a draw after full time. Exhausted sighs, shakes of heads. Dad lit another cigarette, my brother hopped out to take a leak.

Extra time threw in and I was not minding the sheep that had manifested and encircled the car. If they had been wielding guns, I would still not have cared. Dublin were 3 points up in the dying minutes, Mam was professing her usual 'Meath come back, they always come back, come on outa that Dublin!', my brother was tearing the arm off a toy soldier he'd found under the seat and I made a mistake that I would regret for years to come. I made a pact with God that if he made sure that Dublin didn't draw then I would stop plaguing him about my parents getting back together. I was willing to exchange all previous prayers to ensure that there was no draw today. But I guess I wasn't explicit enough in asking that the result go Dublin's way. When Kevin Foley's shot sailed past the Dublin keeper, John O'Leary, with two minutes to go, I panicked. I made the pledge again *please God, don't let it be another draw, you can forget everything else I have asked you for.* When David 'Jinksy' Beggy's point went over, prayers were answered. Only they weren't mine. Meath won.

There was no reconciliation and it was to be a few years before I could get a Dublin jersey of my own.

Celia de Fréine

writes in many genres in both Irish and English. Awards for her poetry include the Patrick Kavanagh Award and Gradam Litríochta Chló Iar-Chonnacht. To date she has published nine collections. Her plays have won numerous awards and are performed regularly. Her film and television scripts have won awards in Ireland and America. *Ceannródaí*, her biography of Louise Gavan Duffy, was published by *Leabhair*COMHAR (2018) who also published her thriller *Cur i gCéill* (2019). Celia won scholarships to attend secondary school. While working in the Civil Service she studied at night for a BA from UCD. She was awarded an MA in Creative Writing from Lancaster University while holding down a teaching position and raising five children. The flash fiction piece included here is from a sequence funded by an Arts Council Covid-19 Response Award. See www.celiadefreine.com

Caoi leis an Ord Tábhachta a chaitheamh i dTraipisí?

Nuair a bheidh sé seo uile thart, cén chaoi a ndéanfar ceiliúradh ar na hoibrithe úd ar phá íseal, gléasta go heasnamhach, a chuir a mbeatha féin i mbaol ar mhaithe le haire a thabhairt do na heasláin agus dóibh siúd a bhí ag fáil bháis? Seans go bhféadfaí ár sochaí a scrúdú tri phriosma ceann eile leis an gceist sin a fhreagairt. Ceann a mhair os cionn céad bliain ó shin, am ar thiarnaí iad na tiarnaí, ar bhuitléirí iad na buitléirí, agus arbh eol do chuile dhuine sa teaghlach a áit nó a háit chuí. Agus cé gur de phór uasal é an tiarna, a bhí ina mháistir ar a raibh timpeall air, ba é an buitléir a bhí i gceannas i ngeall ar a sheiftiúlacht. Ach inar tuigeadh a áit dó.

Samhlaigh teaghlach amháin dá leithéid a sciobadh as a sócúlacht am a ndeachaigh an luamh mhaorga ar a raibh siadsan, an tiarna agus an buitléir, go tóin poill. Agus ar shlog an t-aigéan chuile nóisean den aicme in eangach aimhréidh an mharthanais. Ní hiontas ar bith duit a fhoghlaim gurbh é an buitléir, i ngeall ar a sheiftiúlacht, a tháinig chun cinn i measc na ndaoine longbhriste.

Agus tharla sé go ndeachaigh siad siúd nach raibh seiftiúil i dtaithí ar a bheith ag brath air ar an oileán úd a bhí mar bhaile acu go ceann na mblianta. Agus, ar ndóigh, ar an gcaoi le lútáil air. Chomh fada leis an lá ar tarrtháladh iad agus ar tháinig siad ar ais chuig a seanbhaile, áit a rabhthas ag súil go bhfillfeadh chuile nós is nóisean ar na seandóigheanna. Ina mbíodh an tiarna ina mháistir ar a raibh timpeall air, agus an buitléir i gceannas i ngeall ar a sheiftiúlacht. Ach inar tuigeadh a áit dó.

Níorbh fhada gur léir dóibh siúd a bhí páirteach san eachtra mhuirí, ainneoin a ndíchill, nach bhféadfaidís filleadh ar na seandóigheanna. Agus ní raibh an dara rogha ag an mbuitléir ach an teaghlach a ndearna sé seirbhís air ó bhí sé ina ógánach a thréigean. Na péarlaí a shábháil sé agus é longbhriste ar an oileán úd ina ghlac aige.

Samhlaigh nuair a bheidh sé seo uile thart go bhféadfaí ár sochaí a scrúdú trí phriosma ceann eile. Ceann a mhair céad bliain ó shin ina raibh sé de chumas ag an slánaitheoir luach a shaothair a thuilleamh. Seans go bhféadfaimis céim eile a ghlacadh agus sochaí a shamhlú ina mbeadh sé de chumas ag chuile shlánaitheoir luach a shaothair, nó a saothair, a thuilleamh: dá snífeadh orgánach iasachta, i riocht aitheantas-as-an-obair-a-rinneadh, isteach i moileasc an dímheasa, seans go gcruthófaí sraith néamhann lena chosaint, is go ndéanfaí péarla an cheachta fhoghlamtha de. Dá snífeadh orgánaigh dhearfacha eile isteach i moilisc na n-easnamh, seans go ndéanfaí péarlaí díobhsan freisin. Ar an gcaoi sin seans go gcruthófaí cnuasach péarlaí leis an status quo a iompú bunoscionn.

Le go bhféadfaimis seasamh i sealaíocht ghártha molta in athuair le ceiliúradh a dhéanamh ar thodhchaí úrnua ina mbronnfar luach a saothair ar na hoibrithe úd ar phá íseal, gléasta go heasnamhach, a chuireann a mbeatha féin i mbaol ar mhaithe le haire a thabhairt do na heasláin agus dóibh siúd atá ag fáil bháis.

A Way in Which to Overturn the Pecking Order?

When all this is over how will we celebrate those lowly-paid, inadequately-clad workers who risked their lives while looking after the ill and dying? A way in which to answer that question might be to examine our society through the prism of another. One that existed one hundred years ago when lords were lords, butlers butlers, and everyone in the household knew his or her place. And though the lord, born into a life of privilege, was master of all he surveyed, it was the butler who, by dint of ingenuity, was in charge. But also knew his place.

Imagine one such household, taken from its comfort zone, when the noble yacht on which lord and butler sailed was shipwrecked, the ocean swallowing all notions of class in the tangled net of survival. You won't be surprised to learn it was the butler who, by dint of ingenuity, came to the fore among the castaways.

And the others, lacking in ingenuity, came to rely on him on the island they were to call home for years to come. To kow-tow to him, in fact. Until the day they were rescued and returned to their former home where all customs and notions were expected to return to the way they were before. In which the lord was master of all he surveyed, and the butler, by dint of ingenuity, was in charge. But also knew his place. It wasn't long before all involved in the maritime adventure came to realise that, hard as they tried,

43

they could not revert to their old ways. And the butler had no option but to leave the household he had served since his youth, the pearls he had harvested when castaway on that distant island clasped in his fist.

Imagine, when all this is over, how we might examine our society through the prism of another. One that existed one hundred years ago, in which the saviour was able to earn his just reward. Perhaps we could go a step further and imagine a society in which each saviour was able to earn his or her just reward. Were a foreign organism, in the guise of recognition-for-work-done, to enter the mollusc of disdain, perhaps a layer of nacre might form to protect it and result in a pearl of lesson-learned. Were other positive organisms to enter the molluscs of shortcomings, other pearls might be formed. In this way a cluster of pearls might be created to upend the status quo.

So that we might stand in a relay of thunderous applause once more to celebrate a future normal in which all lowly-paid, inadequately-clad workers, who risk their lives while looking after the ill and dying, receive their just reward.

Stephen James Douglas

was born into a small working-class family in 1988 and grew up in Maghaberry, Craigavon. The son of a carpet fitter, Stephen worked as his father's apprentice before developing a love for literature at the Royal Belfast Academical Institution. Graduating from The Queen's University, Belfast, in 2010 with a joint honours degree in English and Film Studies, Stephen gained a Postgraduate Certificate of Education at Ulster University and has taught in secondary education for eight years. Stephen's poetry has been published in literary magazines including *A New Ulster* and *Automatic Pilot*.

Gaia's Diagnosis

A white room. Two chairs. Evening.
DOCTOR and GAIA are sitting motionless in the chairs.
Enter LOVELOCK carrying a scroll.
Facing the auditorium, LOVELOCK unrolls the scroll and begins to read in a temperate English accent.

LOVELOCK: Humans on the Earth behave in some ways like a pathogenic organism, or like the cells of a tumour or neoplasm. We have grown in numbers and disturbance to Gaia, to the point where our presence is perceptibly disturbing... the human species is now so numerous as to constitute a serious planetary malady. Gaia is suffering from Disseminated Primatemaia, a plague of people...

Exit LOVELOCK.

DOCTOR: [*Turning towards GAIA.*] So we have the biopsies back, and the biopsies do confirm that you have Disseminated Primatemaia.

GAIA: [*Nodding her head.*] Yes.

DOCTOR: [*Moving her chair beside GAIA.*] Are you ok?

GAIA: [*Holding back tears.*] Yes. [*Suddenly overcome with emotion.*] Sorry. [*Straitening in her chair, exhaling deeply.*]

DOCTOR: It's a lot to take it in, it's ok to shed a tear or two...

GAIA: Is it terminal?

DOCTOR: I'm afraid so.

45

Kevin Doyle

is from Cork. From a working-class background, he attended college and later worked in the chemical industry in Ireland and the USA. A stay-at-home dad for many years, he now works at technical writing and as a creative writing teacher in the community sector. He's been a grassroots activist for much of his life, taking part in campaigns such as anti-water tax movement and Repeal 8th / Together 4 Yes. He co-wrote with Spark Deeley the illustrated children's book, *The Worms That Saved The World*— about a collective of earthworms who fight to reclaim their home from a luxury golf course development. He's also the author of two political crime thrillers set in the Cork area—*To Keep A Bird Singing* (2018) and *A River Of Bodies* (2019)—both published by Blackstaff Press. More at www.kevindoyle.ie

The Water War

There were briquette bales in the hall and I could hear the radio; her coat and scarf lay on the stairs. I stood for a moment. The front door was wide open so I called out, but there was no reply. I walked down the hall as far as the kitchen door and saw her, half-bathed in sunlight, standing near the table. She was wearing only jeans and a yellow bra, and her body was twisted in a spiral, in a way that reminded me of a discus thrower. Except that there was no discus in her hand. She was holding a mobile phone and taking pictures, a lot of pictures, of her lower left back.

'Karen,' I asked, 'what are you doing?'

The phone clattered onto the floor. 'Jesus,' she replied, 'the fright you gave me.'

Another time, maybe a month or more after we met, I went to her place. She had read a review of a bottle of wine in the newspaper and had gone out specially to buy it. Laughing, she explained that I had started to make her do things like that. I was pleased; it was an admission of sorts.

We drank the wine slowly. Unexpectedly, she asked, 'When were you happiest in your life?'

I had to think about my answer. It was not a question I had ever been asked before and I was then fifty-one. I am now fifty-two.

'Apart from this moment, you mean?'

'Be truthful.'

'I am,' I said.

She put her hand on my wrist and squeezed it. Hers eyes were green, deeply set. She had a long face, her features pronounced. After a moment she returned to her question. 'Okay, so apart from now?'

I answered that I didn't really know. There had been periods when I was contented, but those were fleeting and were mostly confined to my youth when I was, I suppose, more carefree. I had married in my twenties but it hadn't worked out. When we separated, my wife went to live in America on foot of a lottery Green Card, taking our son with her. I met my son again many years later but we never really clicked. It's been civil between us since and I've stayed in contact but I find myself disappointed, in myself and with him. What I mostly feel now about that matter, about my failed marriage and my son, is regret. It's like I played a part in something important but somehow missed out on what it was all about.

Karen listened and then, after a while, she said, 'For me it was when I was twenty-four. I remember it particularly because I'm now forty-eight. Double those years. I was working in Germany then and I made a lot of money. I travelled on to Greece. I was there nearly six months and I had a boyfriend during some of my time there. Once we were in Santorini. The sand on the beach there is black, from the volcanoes. One evening we were walking along the shore and Bing Crosby was singing 'Strangers in the Night'. The music was coming from a taverna and you could hear it right along that stretch of seashore. We went over and sat down and had some wine and ouzo and then we went back to my place and made love and it was literally the most enjoyable sex I ever, ever had. I gave everything to it. I only wanted to be there and nowhere else. He wasn't really special but I was happy with myself and who I was then. I was a young woman, my life ahead of me.' After a pause she added, 'What's so strange now, you see, I think, is that I never got back to that place again. The happiest time in my life was just that one period, those six months.'

I would call to see her and end up in these places in my mind that I had never been before but have been since; places where you consider your life, how happy you are or were, who made you happy and what happiness actually is. I was pleased though. I felt she was special. A possibility opened up—it was strange to realise it and be in it at the same time—and I remember that I wanted it, I really did. I wanted everything that it could give.

Her main sitting room had a small fireplace with a metal guard in front of it, decorated with coloured flower leaves. On the mantelpiece there were photographs of her daughter, Aisling, many to do with basketball but some for hurling too. There was one beautiful photograph of her with Aisling outside Disneyland in Paris. Her daughter was about eight, I'd say, in the photo. There were none anywhere of him.

She was waiting for a Skype call from Aisling to begin. Her daughter had gone to Australia during the economic crash and had settled in Perth. She had an Irish boyfriend, a guy who worked up in the mines on a week-on, week-off basis. He was away at work and Aisling had just returned from the beach.

The call began. It was a video connection. Aisling was sitting on a recliner in bright sunshine wearing a khaki bikini. At one point she panned her laptop camera around so that we could see more of her place. There were beautiful tropical plants behind her with large green leaves as big as elephants' ears.

Mother and daughter caught up. They talked about Aisling's work. She had got a job with an insurance company and they had suggested they could sponsor her, if she wanted to stay on in Australia. Aisling had a degree but she wasn't keen to make any long term choices right then.

It was nice to hear the two women talk. I realised that Karen missed her daughter much more than she was letting on. I was surprised, though, when I heard her advise Aisling to stay in Australia.

'Don't bother coming back,' she said, 'there's nothing for you in this country now.'

Eventually Karen altered the position of her laptop so that the Skype camera saw me.

'Who's that then?' asked her daughter.

'That's Brendan,' she replied

'Hello Brendan,' said Aisling.

'Hi,' I said.

'I met him at the water tax protest,' explained Karen. 'The big one we had here in the estate. The one I was telling you about. He came out, all the way over here to the south side of the city to help us. Can you believe that? He's from Mayfield.'

Aisling waved to me and I waved back. She looked like her mother, the same bone structure in her face but she had darker hair; she looked exotic with her tan.

'You should both come out here to visit me.'

'I'd like that,' I said immediately. Her mother said nothing. Later I mentioned it to Karen, that maybe it could be a plan for us. We could save our money and do it. I remember it as a terrible moment. It was like I had said something awful. Karen came over to me and put her arms around me and buried her head in my chest. She cried. I asked her what was wrong but she wouldn't tell me. She passed it off a bit later by saying she just missed Aisling a lot and that it got to her sometimes. But I didn't believe her.

I don't know why I did it, but I looked at the photos on her phone. Nothing in particular made me do it but I did it. I looked at photographs from weeks earlier, from that time when I had seen her looking like a discus thrower in her kitchen. I looked further back as well and I came to the photos that I had taken of Karen on the day when we first met. I very nearly hadn't gone to the

48

protest that morning—that was the strange thing. Just something made me get off my arse for a change and go over there. That was what I thought about as I looked at those photos—those beautiful photos from that day.

I looked further back. There were more selfies of her lower back and an occasional one was on target. I saw just a red spot. Tiny, really. I didn't quite understand what I was looking at until a few days later. I had stayed over and when Karen got out of bed in the morning I looked for the mark and saw it immediately on her lower back. But it wasn't small any longer. It looked sore and uneven, and big.

Later, over breakfast, I asked her, 'What are those photos on your phone about, the ones of your back? There's such a lot of them.'

'You looked at my phone?'

'Why do you take them?'

She flung her cup at me and it struck me on the side of the forehead, a glancing blow. I was stunned.

'Get out,' she screamed. 'Get out.'

I went. I closed the door behind me and stood outside on her front path. There was low winter light in the sky, the estate quiet. I remember holding my head. My forehead was cut.

She was sitting outside her house on a mauve two-person sofa. There, on its own, the piece of furniture looked like something from a movie set. Garish, worn. The sun was shining and she looked relaxed, bemused by the ruckus. I didn't pay that much attention to her at first because there was so much else happening.

Across from where she was sitting a man lay prone on the road and he was screaming. He had everyone's attention.

'Over my dead body, over my dead body,' he shouted.

Above him, precariously positioned on the rear of a flatbed truck, a yellow mini-digger was threatening to dismount along tracks that would have taken the heavy machine directly onto the belly of the prone protestor. There was pandemonium. Local people were jostling and shouting at the Irish Water workers, trying to push them back.

A woman pounded on the truck's cabin window. 'No water meters here. No water meters here. No to austerity.'

When the Gardaí arrived, the crowd moved closer together around the truck, as if for protection. I stood back, a bit unsure, uncertain. I was really worried for the man on the road. I could see an accident happening, a life being lost.

During a lull, a voice called out, 'Would you take a picture of me?'

I looked and saw a woman, a bit younger than me, sitting on her sofa. 'I want to send it to my daughter in Australia. I want to prove to her that we're doing something at last, that we're fighting austerity.'

I went over reluctantly, and she handed me her mobile phone. She posed. 'Take one this way, now that way, now the other way.' We did side-profile to the right, side-profile to the left. Finally, she swept her long hair back behind her head and asked, 'How's this?'

'You think that will work for your daughter?' I said.

She smiled. 'That's not for my daughter, it's for you.'

I laughed and looked at the photo. 'Very beautiful,' I said showing her. 'Charmer.'

She stood, straightened her clothes and pulled her cardigan closed around her. 'Will you have a cup of tea?'

I looked over at the ruckus. It was stalemate. 'I will,' I answered.

'Then hold the fort.' She pointed to her sofa and fetched a pillow, plumping it up for me to sit against.

'The water supply stop cock is directly underneath the sofa. Don't let anyone near it. Austerity's not coming in my gate.'

I sat down. The sofa was positioned on the public footpath just outside her front gate. Right along, up and down the estate, as far as I could see, her neighbours were similarly camped outside their houses on similar items of home furniture. It was a big protest. Just two houses further on, they had the full kitchen table set put out and were playing cards.

Further along again, near a stretch of park, the invading army of Irish Water meter installers were parked at a standstill; flatbed trucks, JCBs and jeeps were lined up army-column style. A few men in suits were talking to an older man with white hair in a high-vis vest.

'Over-my-dead-body' was still screaming with all his might from close by. It was becoming clear, however, that he had won the day; the installation of water meters had been stopped.

'I'm Karen,' she said when she came back to ask me if I wanted milk or sugar.

'Just milk.'

She handed me her phone with all her photos on it. 'Choose one for my daughter.'

When she returned, I showed her the one that I felt made the strongest statement. It showed Karen sitting defiantly cross-legged looking across the road at the protest. She was neither scolding or smiling in the photo. She looked determined.

'Perfect,' she agreed.

Now and then, I make the journey again. I wait near the betting shop at the Cotton Ball for the number 8 bus and when it comes I pay the fare and climb up to the upper deck. I like to get the seat that I had the day that I met her—

row two from the front window, on the pavement side. If it's already taken, I take the next nearest available seat.

Once the bus moves off, I rest my cheek against the glass. If it's a cold day the glass is covered with condensate and I cannot see much. I don't mind. I know what's to be seen all along the route anyway; I know that well now.

Finally, I get to Wilton and get off. I walk down the road, under the flyover and then I am on the edge of the estate, where the protest-stand-off happened, where 'Over my dead body' made his stand.

Sometimes, just then, just there, I'm afraid to go on. Eventually I do. I walk as far as her terrace and then up to her house. I often go as far as her front door. It is quiet all around there now. No one has their furniture out on the road anymore. The water war is over and we won. Now her house is for sale.

Linda Ervine

was born into a working-class Protestant family in East Belfast. She is the first Irish Language Officer to be based in a loyalist area. When she began learning Irish in 2011, no one would have conceived of the idea of an Irish language centre in the heart of East Belfast, but despite many difficulties the centre is now one of the largest providers of Irish language classes in Belfast. In 2013 Linda received the Roll of Honour in the Aisling Award for her work promoting the Irish language. In 2015 she received the Community Relations Council (CRC) Civic Leadership Award and in 2020 she received the Eastside Community Champion Award. Prior to her present role as manager of the Turas project, she trained as a teacher and taught English in a secondary school in East Belfast. Linda is presently undertaking a part-time degree in Irish.

Education

When I was very young, I remember asking my mum, why did my older brother have a middle name but I didn't? Her reply was that when my brother grew up, he might get a good job, and then he would need a middle name. At the time I was quite happy with that explanation because I didn't understand that what my mother was saying was that because I was a girl, I would never get a good job and I would never need a middle name. The only hope for me was to someday marry someone who would have a good job.

My experience of school was not positive. I suppose I was what might be called nowadays a school refuser, but in the 1970s you were simply branded a truant. When I did attend school I seldom had a book or a pen and I didn't bring in homework or bring back books or wear the proper uniform and in the end the school became fed up with me and expelled me. If truth be told it wasn't the only school that I was expelled from. However, at that time, it wasn't an issue for me as I was glad to be free from it.

During my teenage years, education was not my top priority, in fact it wasn't even on my list. I had no ambitions and few interests apart from underage drinking, discos, boys and smoking. By the age of sixteen I was pregnant, and the life of a single mum loomed ahead.

After my daughter was born, I moved into a house down the street from my grandparents. It was on the interface, and ours was the last Protestant house before the no man's land that divided the two sides. There was no peace wall at that time and windows were smashed regularly by the competing groups of young people who entertained themselves by throwing bricks at unsuspecting houses.

If there was rioting in the area, or someone witnessed three or more people breaking your windows, then the police arranged for them to be replaced, and if your windows were smashed three times then you could get grids. Now, this system didn't work particularly well as unfortunately the perpetrators didn't always carry out their raids when witnesses were about and tended not to leave a calling card. Because of that I spent many weeks living in darkness with boarded up windows, unable to afford to pay for replacements.

At the back of our house the kitchen was a lean-to with a corrugated plastic roof. One Christmas a brick came through it, leaving a large gaping hole for the rain to come through. I remember sitting on the floor and crying. I was eighteen years old.

The years that followed brought marriage, a move to a house around the corner, two more children and working as a cleaner in various places. At twenty-one, after the birth of my son, I made an attempt at returning to education, enrolling on a course at the local college. For some reason my then mother-in-law felt that this was a threat to family life and said to my husband, 'What are you letting her do that for?' and although he didn't respond to it at the time, a few weeks later, after a row, he took my books and burned them in the fire. I just didn't seem to have the same interest after that.

The next stages in my life were depression, anxiety, agoraphobia, fear and illness. Life was a black hole that I couldn't climb out of, but in my early thirties another venture into education became my escape. This time I enrolled on a computer course. My ambition was to get a job in an office. I didn't know what people did in offices, but I thought that computers would be involved. I had no idea then that taking the plunge to sign up for a class would have such an impact on the rest of my life.

Sitting in a classroom with other people was very daunting for me at that time. I was still struggling with mental health issues and had no confidence. I had never even touched a computer and it appeared to me that everyone else seemed to know what they were doing. As I nervously awaited instructions from the teacher, the rest of the class were switching on their machines and opening up programmes. I felt so inadequate and stupid, but before long I too was confidently clicking on the mouse and typing on the keyboard. This was the beginning of what would be a very long journey.

By the following year I had enrolled for GCSEs, and from then on every small success, every certificate, every good mark and positive comment written at the bottom of a page, spurred me on year after year. Each September I loved the adventure of new courses and new opportunities. After achieving all 'A' grades at GCSE, I was encouraged to enrol on an Access Course, but when I realised that it was for access to university I decided against it as I had no ambitions in that direction. I wasn't good enough or clever enough to even think about going to university. Instead I enrolled to do three A-levels: English Literature, Politics and Psychology. Somewhere on this part of the journey I changed my mind about what I could achieve and decided to apply to Queens.

At the beginning of September 1998 my first husband and I went to the open day at Queen's University, and I remember walking around the various buildings in awe of all that went on there and of the possibilities that were opening up in front of me. As I talked to various people from the different departments, my husband stood back looking uncomfortable and urging me to hurry up.

When we returned home I put on my overall and walked over to my job in a chippie on the Cregagh Road, my mind still buzzing with the excitement of my visit to the university. It was a beautiful sunny evening, and after the tea-time rush I was helping to clear up when my husband arrived at the door of the shop. He was drunk and he called me outside, where he started shouting. There was no mention of our visit that day, but when he punched me I got the message, and somewhere inside me I decided that nothing would stop me from going to university.

In my first week at Queens I explored the campus, filled with a mixture of fear and excitement. I remember bumping into someone who had been in one of my GCSE classes at college. He was an older man who frequently informed the class that he had a degree in science. One day the teacher announced that we would be studying Shakespeare's Macbeth. I was terrified, and I thought seriously about making for the door. However, the man with a degree in science took it all in his stride.

'I have the complete works of Shakespeare on my bookshelf at home,' he told us all. I was very impressed.

Our teacher smiled at him and said, 'Do you indeed, have you ever taken them down and read them?'

It turned out that despite my absences at school I had a bit of natural ability, and unfortunately the man with the degree in science didn't. One day during class the teacher asked me to show him how to embed quotes into a text. I saw the look of horror on his face that the likes of me was being asked to show him anything.

Now here he was again, a member of the P.E. Centre at Queens. Obviously surprised to see me, and that I wasn't one of the cleaners, he said, 'How did you get here, dear?'

And being from East Belfast, I replied, 'I done my A Levels and I passed them all.'

He then turned to his friend and said, 'Good God, they'd let anybody in here now!'

And because everyone around me used 'I done', as it is part of our dialect, I had no idea that it was regarded as wrong. Sadly, at that time, I thought his comments were fair and that I wasn't good enough to be there.

Although suffering from a terrible lack of confidence, I persevered, and by the time I reached the last year of my degree I had decided to apply for a place on the PGCE. One of my final year modules was Sociolinguistics, and I found it particularly interesting reading about the different types of registers that we all use. During one of the classes there was a discussion on colloquial terms used locally. The lecturer mentioned how 'did' and 'done' are used by speakers in Belfast, and of course I was now very aware of this, but then she said, 'and seen and saw' and everyone smiled and nodded. And I thought what's wrong with seen and saw? Suddenly I felt again like an outsider, I wasn't part of this exclusive club that understood these things. I wondered how they knew and I didn't? Who had told them? Why did I not know these things? Did I give myself away every time I opened my mouth? What other rules were there that I wasn't even aware of? How could I apply for teaching when I didn't even know that the rules existed!

I'm very pleased to be able to say that I achieved my goals. I completed my degree and then spent a year training as a teacher. I was appointed as an English teacher in a girls' secondary school in East Belfast, a school which had refused to accept me as a pupil during my troubled teenage years. I taught for nine years and I thought that would be my career for life, but then I was introduced to the Irish language and that began a love affair that led me away from teaching and into my present post as an Irish language development officer. This was part of the journey that I never could have envisaged when I took those first tentative steps into adult education.

Being involved with the Irish language has changed my life dramatically. I cannot begin to describe the pleasure that learning a language brings as you go from being a total beginner, struggling with the difficult sounds of new words and then achieving increasing amounts of fluency. I am so grateful that even though it came late in life, I was given the opportunity to learn Irish. It opened a door to a world of new experiences and new friends. Unfortunately, as well as gaining friends, learning the language has caused me to lose friends and made me a target for those who regard Irish as the language of the enemy. I have learnt that sometimes in life when you decide to journey along a different path, it threatens others, but there is no turning back.

I remember many years ago listening to a Scottish female poet reading a poem which described education as a journey to a new land, where at first you feel far from home in unfamiliar territory, but then you gradually settle and adjust to new ways and customs. It is only later that you realise you can never return home as you are now an alien in your own land. This description resonated with me and my own journey which started when I was still working in the chippie, when none of my friends had an education, when my expectations in life were different. The journey I am on has changed me, and although I didn't consciously reject the life that I was part of, I was desperate for something different, for something better.

At times the people around me were more aware of the change in me than I was. I began to want to talk about other things; my world was broadening and some of my friends found it more and more difficult to relate to me and me to them. Unfortunately, sometimes on your journey to somewhere else you leave a little bit of who you are behind and those close to you are unable or unwilling to journey with you.

When I was a teenager I believed that education was just something else that 'they' were making you do. It would be many years later before I realised that learning was a door into another life. The education I have received, the qualifications I have obtained, lifted me out of poverty by not only providing me with an income but with a passion for learning and a drive to inspire others.

'Education is for improving the lives of others and for leaving your community and world better than you found it.'
—Marian Wright Edelman

Attracta Fahy

grew up on a farm in East Galway, giving her a strong work ethic, and a sensitivity to human difficulties. She lives in County Galway, works as a psychotherapist, and is mother to three children. She first trained as a nurse, specialising and working as a hospice nurse, later training in social care, working in Social Services during the nineties, where she was instrumental in turning the service into a client-centred service. She worked with many complex issues before training as a psychotherapist, after which she was employed in agencies supporting the under represented. Attracta continues to advocate for, and work with, the most vulnerable in society.

Mothering Through The Pandemic

It's been weeks since my eldest son posted on Instagram. He is thirty-four, and I still worry about him living six thousand miles away, in Los Angeles, in a country in turmoil. He works as an anaesthesiologist. The frontline is a very traumatic place to be as the coronavirus sweeps across the United States. It had been contained in California, but as everything opened up, a new wave emerged.

I miss his posts; that one daily photo is part of how I connect to reassure myself that he is ok.

We talked over the months, his pain in not being able to save patients, daily deaths from the virus, ten in one day. He calls work a death camp.

'It's terrible to lose a patient; even worse watching them die without loved ones. Seeing body bags waiting to be removed is the worst, no actually, it's when you have patients waiting for a ventilator, knowing another of your patients has to die first, it's awful mum!'

We have all heard these stories, the mayhem in hospitals, tragedy, loss, and pain. We hear daily numbers of those who died, and the loss of traditional rituals when burying our dead. This virus, like a comet, came shooting in, wreaking havoc; every tragic story reflects how susceptible we are to trauma. It's as if there's a broken mirror spinning somewhere in orbit, reflecting back the state of our world. Not least, showing us who cares about the vulnerable in our society, and who cares about humanity.

Hearing the story of others is one thing, hearing your son's experience is somewhat different. His words hammer and splinter through my body. My pain is knowing that I cannot take it from him. So, I stay strong, seeing the importance of mirroring to children how to face adversity.

It's difficult to listen to horror, but knowing how to listen when one needs to be heard, encourages me to give that space. Offloading a burden, or sharing turmoil, relieves pressure and distress from the perpetual tumult

57

of trauma, which many health care workers have experienced.

Being aware of how trauma gets into the body if not heard, often presenting as illness, anxiety or depression, I stay mindful, creating the space he needs to share. It's amazing how a person finds strength when heard with empathy.

Growing up on a farm, and having a background in nursing, gave me a strong foundation to accept the darker, traumatic side of life. Besides, being a caretaker is my nature. This can be a curse, or a blessing; right now it's the latter.

These days when I phone, he rarely answers, instead sends a message: 'All ok? I'm at work.'

His response when asked how he is, is usually:

'Grand, really busy!'

Grand means so many things for us Irish, but in this case I take it to mean, 'getting on with it.'

Occasionally, I receive a flurry of texts updating me on how terrible it is, but once again—he's grand. We used to chat weekly, as we both have a mischievous nature, and we'd laugh a lot. Now it's several weeks since we've spoken.

I suspect he doesn't want to break down and cry, as he has done several times, he possibly doesn't want to feel vulnerable right now. He lost his closest friend, a family friend, to Covid, so we are all grieving. He also lost two colleagues.

Maybe there is wisdom in not calling; we have to find our own individual path through this grief. Separateness gives us space to do this, and there is solace in knowing we are there for one another when needed. I know it is difficult for him to keep up a pretence, and as a mother I pick up on his mood—he knows I will ask. He needs his defence and persona to get through.

I think of the quote from Ghalib:

My fingernails are clawing down toward my heart again.
It must be the right time for planting red tulips.

I sow seeds every spring in my garden, just as my mother used to sew on her Singer sewing machine. I could have been a dressmaker, but I refused, wanting to find my own identity. This year I have one mauve poppy in every pot. I'm sure I sowed several together, and joke that they too must have picked up on social distancing.

Thankfully, I'm not neurotic about my garden; it's been my haven during this pandemic.

I was busy planting in April, painting pots, listening to birds, spotting different types, and breeds, as they got on with the business of building nests on my roof, and in trees. I was feeling creative, and then everything changed after losing our friend Robby. I lost momentum. These days I sit out at the table, and watch the garden grow wild.

The birds have progressed to a different stage, their chicks hatched, and preparing to leave the nest. My brood have already left, coming and going, except for my eldest, his life now in America.

My second son, who is twenty-four, had just moved to Dublin to start an internship in public relations when lockdown began. He spent eleven weeks in a house with three others, all working from home, before he could travel past two kilometres. Although not on the frontline, this in itself was a huge challenge, requiring negotiation, patience, and tolerance. I don't feel his age group, who have an innate need to socialise, have been given enough credit. He also says everything is grand.

'How are you?' I ask. 'Grand mum, how are you?' he replies.

That's it, unless he needs to rant, then he sends a text asking me to call, which is not often as he has plenty of friends.

Since things began to open up, he has come home every weekend. He misses the gym, his friends, socialising, wants a new tattoo, and now talks about saving to go on a psychedelic retreat, in the hope of gaining enlightenment. This is something we would all love, but few escape having to navigate the infernos life throws at us, before arriving in Ithaca, if we ever do. I rely on my garden, the birds, and the old stone walls covered in moss.

I'm working on getting him to see that I can save him expense, that the urgency in his seeking answers is the existential question we all have, and he will have to paddle the river of life, until he sees he is both question, and answer. I make it sound complex because he likes a challenge.

He has already holidayed in Mexico visiting ancient sites, so I know he has a genuine curiosity, and who am I to say he will not be the next guru, but it is important I do my job as a mother, and keep him earthed.

I told him I was proof that one can have a psychedelic experience without taking psychedelics; after all he has grown up listening to me talking to flowers, and trees, in fact everything non human. Maybe I'm responsible for his deep search for knowledge. I was always observing out loud:

'Can you smell the earth?'

'Oh my gosh, look at the moon!

Oh my god, isn't the sky beautiful?

To which he'd reply:

'Yes mum!'

'Yes, mum, it's lovely, now can you look where you're going.'

'Oh for god's sake mum, can you stop looking at the sky while you're driving!'

It's hard not to notice a sea of cobalt blue, its glacier white puffs, or the varied fires of the sun.

The purple petunia outside my kitchen window speaks to me in its own language, flower language I call it, when colours speak to me. It's the best language right now in a world with too many words. It doesn't have a scent, which means my focus is more visual. The words of T.S. Eliot from *The Waste Land* come to mind, in 'What the Thunder said', and I wonder what the colour says—'Nothing!'

It says absolutely nothing, and yet it speaks. How can it be that delicate petals of light, dark, varied tones of purple can say without words 'It will be ok, all will be well?' And I think of Julian of Norwich, 'All shall be well, and all manner of things shall be well.'

This gives me strength, admiring beauty for what it is: purple, the colour of the third eye chakra, intuition, and peace.

My focus is always balancing between different worlds: it might be contemplating a red geranium, pink hydrangea, blue agapanthus, a bird calling in the distance, like the cuckoo I hear all through May, a red chaffinch foraging near my feet, or the brown spotted belly of a thrush. There is a murderous, consoling beauty in nature.

Perhaps we can't cope with beauty, or know how to manage it. Ancient people were good with beauty, particularly the Greeks, but beauty to a capitalist world is something to be coveted, or destroyed.

I am immensely comforted by my garden; grateful nature still thrives where it can.

This was my daughter's final year in college, so when everything shut down, she had to adjust to online classes and projects. Again, it was challenging, but she has good friends, and they supported each other. All I could do was be there, and cook wholesome dinners. She loves mashed potato, salmon, and homemade burgers. I was tied to the cooker.

When she finished her exams, a new anxiety set in. She had to be with herself; the concerts, festivals she had booked for this summer were cancelled, as well as her plans to take a year out, to go to Vancouver with friends.

After weeks of turmoil, spending hours walking alone, painting and decorating her room, playing loud music, repeating the same songs, she realised she wanted to break up with her boyfriend. That was two months ago and it has been heartbreaking to see her hurt, because she had hurt someone whom she loved, but felt she was no longer in love.

I struggle to see my daughter as an adult, the youngest of my three children, and though she is almost twenty-three, her tiny frame, dainty face, and the fact she is exactly five foot, leave her looking no more than twelve. She laughs, and enjoys being cute. It is only when she speaks, I know she is an adult.

It was lovely having her for the summer, doing special things like going for picnics, walks, and later as things began to open up, taking scenic drives.

I take a back seat with my daughter, letting her ask for advice if she needs, and always careful what I say, as she can react easily if I say something wrong. Of course, I never know what the wrong thing might be, so it's best to say very little, and keep my heart open to listening, responding with empathy, mirroring back what I hear are her own thoughts.

She decided she wanted to move to the city, especially as she was looking for work. It was too isolated for her in the countryside with only two buses a day, and where she hadn't much freedom.

She found a room, and is now living with three other girls, none of whom she had known prior to this. Her eldest brother gave her money as a gift for finishing college, so she used that and savings to pay her deposit and a month's rent in advance. She is full of fear right now, but is facing it, and very much needs my encouragement.

I helped her move in, and while I have met her most days, I am faced with the reality that I am once again living alone. I miss her. I would love to have her at home, keep her safe from my fear of what could happen. My task as mother is to help her find her independence.

When I think of this, I feel a wave of sadness, get an image of a cord being cut, severing a bond that existed long before she was born. It's difficult when your youngest child leaves.

This is the pain I must bear, if she is to grow.

I was to be in LA this week for my son's graduation; instead he graduated on Zoom, at two o'clock in the morning. I joined the presentations, as he and his fellow graduates did from the hospital. It was nice to see they were together when they couldn't have their families with them.

It was a bit surreal. I got dressed up for the occasion, but they only saw my head. There was no after party; however, there was huge gratitude, gratitude too to be alive, and much humility.

Neumann is most likely right when he said in his considerations for humanity, that if the world was to survive, it needed a new ethic, one where we take personal responsibility for the mess we have created. Humility is a good start, and nature appears to have jump-started us into some reflective process.

In many ways this pandemic gave us the opportunity to contemplate, pay more attention to what is important: relationships, family, friendship, and nature. Our ancestors had a wisdom we seem to have taken for granted, forgotten, or made unconscious. We have an opportunity now to make it conscious.

At the outset of this crisis, I had begun to adjust to the reality that my children have grown up, feeling they don't need me anymore; I was carving out a different life for myself. I had been contemplating what I would do as an ageing woman to find meaning and purpose after over ten years parenting alone.

I work as a mental health professional, which is challenging at times, and very fulfilling, but demands quite a lot of commitment. It is also important to have my own needs met, to give expression to my creativity. In the past few years, I'd begun to enjoy developing writing skills, attending workshops, and meeting new people. Writing introduced me to a different inner world. This ceased in April, when I was confronted with managing the effect of the pandemic on people's mental health. It seems to be exacerbated as we come out of lockdown. There is a lot of depression, anxiety and stress being expressed, not just about the virus; it's about survival and learning to adjust to change. With no instruction book, I was learning how to get through, while also guiding others.

My role as mother changed when my children became adults. As they began to create their own path, they didn't rely on me so much—yet, when this crisis struck, home is where they turned for support. Mother is still who they need when they are overwhelmed.

My mother died when I was my daughter's age. Even without her showing me how to parent adult children, her wisdom, and strength, carries through.

Declan Geraghty

is a writer, poet and spoken word performer. Born and raised in Dublin, he grew up in Neilstown, Clondalkin. He has lived in Madrid for eleven years, where he worked as an English teacher, but is now back living in Dublin. He has been involved in some poetry and short story anthologies, most notably *Dublin In the Coming Times* and *The Flying Superhero Clothes Horse*. He found it has been a huge struggle growing up working class in a country which he finds very middle-class driven. He has been looked down on or missed out on opportunities, either because of his accent or where he was from. Ireland has a problem with class prejudice and he hopes to be a part of breaking it with his writing.

Nine hour stroll

I'd go into that bookshop now, but that security guard is always staring me out of it. The fact that that weirdo was in the jacks this morning meant I couldn't have a proper shave or a wash. Which makes me look even more of a suspicious looking type. Ye need a bit of warm in some places some days. A bit of heat. It's not that I'm afraid of him or anything like that. On the contrary I'd slap the head of em if he tried anything. There's just something about him. Something negative, something brewing inside him. Something dangerous. I don't think most of the others notice. They're mostly either drunk, stoned or on gear. Some that do have a bit of sense about them are on methadone, basically trying to keep their brains from spilling out of their skulls; they have enough problems trying to get to the next sentence they were chatting about. Sometimes you'd be in mid sentence with someone and they'd completely forget what they were saying.

They'd even forget that they were talking to you and suddenly start looking around the room or checking something on their phone. If you'd try to finish the chat or sew them subtly back into the conversation you'd just end up feeling a bit awkward somehow.

My technique about using keywords to get them back into the conversation usually worked, and I could have been a fairly good sociologist or economist if I was from a family with a few quid. One with a bit of cop on.

I talked with me Ma briefly about college after me Leaving Cert. College, ye lazy bastard, ye don't want to work! And that's how a lot of working-class kids views on education are sculpted through their young lives. There isn't a lot to look forward to or dream about once you get to a certain age. Especially when you follow the herd; it just gets painful and laborious with time. Then they have the middle class sniggering at them, calling them scum or lazy. Just because they use substances to escape a life of ten euros an hour, or a life on the dole, maybe thrown out on some CE scheme for an extra twenty euros a week. A hamster on the wheel so the government can say you're productive.

Town is warm today. It has that smell, that polluted summer smell of the bus engines revving up at the terminuses in the heat. They rev and doors swoosh open and the crowds fall in. They go to their homes on mid Friday afternoons. Preparing for a night out with friends or loved ones. The cinema or a few beers. Maybe some shopping and a bit of Netflix later on. I've only ever seen it in a mate's once. Supposed to be all the rage these days. So they say. They go home to gaffs, but I stay here. Roaming around town until seven o'clock, until this place opens. Every day ten to seven. Every day.

What's that film called with Bill Murray? *Groundhog Day*, that's it. I'm living that. The women that walk around town. They're foreign, from every country you can think of, not like the eighties. I think I saw my first black person at around seven. Dublin was another world in my childhood and teenage years. It seems like an eternity ago now, even though I'm only forty. These women. Their dark skin and hazel eyes. They're always smiling. Beautiful white toothy smiles, and I wonder sometimes if I was cleaned up and with a career could I pull one of them? Surely I could, I was good with the birds in me teenage years and early twenties, but then the drink took hold.

It gets hold before you even realise it. Even being off it a year it still lingers there in the back of your mind like some kind of strange absentee landlord. Waiting for you to drink again. A payment to your self-consciousness for the suffering you endure in this life.

I bought a few bottles of non-alcoholic beer and sat in the Phoenix Park, near the cricket club. There were lots of crowds out, sitting in groups, taking in the summer sun. That smell of the earth, warming up after seasons of rain, hit my senses. That smell. It felt like freedom. Like success. But it also reminded me of the summers of my teenage years. The drinking cider in fields, strong cider. Really heavy days. Alcohol induced days. Friends lost days. Girlfriends lost days.

Violent, don't know how the argument started, stale beer on dark tarmac days. Rizla skins tossed on the grass days. I smoked so much weed I can't taste the cigarette days. Kissing Denise tongue twirling chewing gum behind the church graveyard days. Twenty Major and John Player Blue days. We've only got Benson and Hedges says the shopkeeper days. I can't believe I had the nerve to think I could be something days. I used to think these people were animals. Then I ended up one of them. The madness and sloppiness that comes with alcohol. You can't really see it. I just seem normal and then it falls all around you. Collapses when you least expect it. And you're left with nothing.

I lay down. Sometimes the non-alcoholic beers were a waste. You somehow craved more but got nothing in return. Ironic in a way, but a dream for capitalism. The clouds looked like some kind of war going on a biblical scale. They were fluffy and light before the baby blue sky, but there was an intensity there. Seagulls flew high in the sky. They made that noise in the distance by the Liffey at Heuston station. That nasal beak noise. I didn't know whether I loved it or hated it.

A guy walked close by with his dog. A little French bulldog. He looked like an Eastern European man. He had a puffed-out kind of aggressiveness in his walk. It amused me how someone with that type of hard chaw persona could have such a gay- looking dog. Europeans just didn't get it sometimes. I pointed towards the ground at him. The guy with the dog looked at the ground and I just kept pointing. Then I laughed. The guy moved off aggressively, realising he'd been duped into looking at something that wasn't there. I sniggered to myself. Made ye look, ye bleeding dope ye.

Big cars, big beautiful shiny cars, new shapely cars passed through the park in the distance. That one big road that went though the centre of it. I thought about Davey, and what happened that day. He would be about twenty-three years dead now. It would be around this month it fell as well, mid-July. That fight that night, how he died. Nobody ever knew it was me. It just happened. The fight we had, over nothing. The usual. Just the usual. Fighting because of the drink. No real reason or big dramatic moral dilemma or double cross. Just a scrap. A mill up that went too far.

I never told anyone it was me. A tragic death in the papers, poor young innocent Davey they all said. He wasn't innocent at all. He'd rob your gaff and kill your bleeding granny for a few quid, but poor young Davey. The community loved him, all his neighbours were very fond of him. I don't remember his neighbours being fond of him. They were afraid of him more like and just humoured him because they knew he was mad and most probably dangerous. A quiet, very quiet shy type of lad. Shy me arse, he came across quiet because he didn't want to talk to anybody. Usually because he was either skagging or completely hungover.

It was six o'clock now. I'd make a slow walk back to the kip for seven. I tied my jumper around my waist and walked very slowly. So slowly that people looked at me cautiously. I was beginning to smell a little bit of BO under my arms. I knew that roll-on had hardly anything left in it, but I rushed this morning because that creepy bloke Willow was in the jacks. I wondered had the name something to do with the film Willow, but it turns out his name is just William. I wondered why they didn't just call him Willie, but at the same time I didn't really care; once he wasn't near me that was the main thing.

I walked past kids with their exhausted-looking parents, jumping and scurrying and getting up to mischief. I sometimes wished I was one again. Somebody to look after me. To not have the pressures of adulthood weighing you down all the time. To be free and innocent once again. It's when the innocence goes, happiness goes with it I thought.

I gave a good-looking blonde woman a smile as I walked past her, but she completely ignored me. She looked past me with a shrug like I wasn't even there. I walked past a pub and for a split second I felt like stopping, turning, and saying the hell with it. But I didn't, I just kept walking. The cons far outweighed the pros on that one, I'd learned from experience far too many times.

I just begged for that relief sometimes, that spiritual relief two or three pints brought. That little piece of pub heaven. It always went awful after those three pints, it always went loud and heavy. Loud, heavy and spluttering saliva, spraying heavy. Mispronouncing, slurring words, black-out gibberish heavy. That's why I kept walking, but I missed those two or three pints. Even if they couldn't exist in my world. Those three pints. I still missed them.

I got to the door of the kip. It was, amazingly, open. It was six fifty-five and it was open. Jesus, I thought, there's a first for everything. In all my time there, it never opened one second before seven.

Kathy was talking to me while I was going down the hall. That stinking aul hall. A bleach that hung in the air. That stuck to everything. That bleach you could briefly taste on your cup when you had a cup of tea. Not strong enough to poison you, but strong enough to put you off your cup of scald.

And Kathy talked, she never stopped talking. It was her way. It was enough to make your nerves bad. You mostly never listened.

But this time your ears pricked up a little, to hear the words that she was given a place by the council. And how she was waiting thirteen years. There was happiness in your reply to her, but you also felt a bit of jealousy. And even though you were jealous you knew it was wrong, and you felt a bit ashamed for feeling like that. You told her you were delighted for her and tried to feign your happiness as enthusiastically as possible, without coming across false.

You eventually get to the toilets and Willow is by the sink, splashing a bit of water on his face and hair. Great day, isn't it, nods Willow to you. Nice to get a bit of sun. I seen you in the park earlier, having a beer. I was going to go over to you, but you looked like you were just relaxing, flaking out, so I didn't want to bother you, he said. Maybe Willow is alright, after all, I thought.

Liz Gillis

Historian and author Liz Gillis is from the Liberties. She works as a Researcher for the History Show on RTE Radio. Liz was the Historical Consultant for the new Hyatt Centric: The Liberties hotel, and runs 'Revolution in Dublin Walking Tours'. She was a Curatorial Assistant in RTE, specialising in researching the Easter Rising, and a tour guide for many years in Kilmainham Gaol.

Liz is the author of six books including, *Women of the Irish Revolution* and *The Hales Brothers and the Irish Revolution*. Liz has worked as a researcher on numerous publications, television and radio documentaries covering the period.

Liz is a member of the Liberties Cultural Association, a voluntary group which was set up to promote the history of the Liberties. They recently organised the first Liberties International Women's Day Festival. In 2018 Liz was a recipient of the Lord Mayor's Award for her contribution to history.

The Liberties: We Don't Eat Our Young Here Anymore

From the time I was a kid, my dad always said to me, 'Be proud of where you come from.' I'm from the Liberties in Dublin's South inner-city, a working-class community. My family, like so many in the Liberties, has been here for at least five generations. The Liberties is the oldest community in Dublin; it has been in existence since the 12th century. It got its name when King Henry II granted a Liberty in the area in memory of Thomas à Becket, who was murdered by the king's supporters in Canterbury Cathedral. The abbey founded in his name was near present-day Thomas Street. The Liberty lay outside the walls of the medieval city of Dublin. This basically meant the area had control over its own affairs and did things its own way, a trait which can still be found today.

In its near 1,000-year history the area has seen some highs and many lows. But the Liberties has proven its resilience time and again when those in positions of power had written it off, and that is due to the incredible community spirit of the people who call the Liberties home.

It is an area that has a rich, vibrant history. The Liberties is a melting pot; it attracted people from all over Ireland, and beyond, and welcomed them. All that came and went left their mark in some way. You can tell the history of the fight for Irish independence by just walking up Thomas Street. We have a connection to all the Irish revolutionaries. Most famously, Robert Emmet was executed on Thomas Street in 1803 after his failed rebellion. The local story goes that after being beheaded, his head rolled down Bridgefoot Street hill into the Liffey. There was no such thing, but it makes a good story. The country's leading industrialists set up shop in the Liberties: Guinness, Jacob's, Powers, etc. Elements of the Birr Telescope were made in Cork Street at William Spence's Ironworks. The first maternity home on the south side of the city was the Coombe hospital, founded by philanthropist Margaret Boyle. The first children's playground in Ireland was built in Pimlico, by Lady Brabazon, the wife of the Earl of Meath. Artists, musicians, authors, politicians (the first President of the Irish Free State was W.T. Cosgrave, who was from James's Street), actors, revolutionaries and many others have come from the Liberties.

But to outsiders, the Liberties always had a stigma. There was a time, not too recently, that some would look down on those who came from the Liberties. And it was said many a time, 'Jaysus, they eat their young there'. But that was their prejudice, not mine, nor the people I knew. Growing up in the Liberties was, for me, a fantastic experience; it shaped me. I was surrounded by salt of the earth people; I still am. And as kids we were so lucky to have so many great people fighting our corner.

The Liberties as we know it was nearly lost in the 1960s due to Dublin Corporation's road widening scheme. Whole streets were at risk of being decimated for dual carriageways. People like Larry Dillon and John Gallagher, two Liberties legends, put a stop to that. The Corporation thought that no one would put up a fight against their plans. By God they were wrong. Dillon and Gallagher organised the community and they won; Bridgefoot Street has to be the shortest dual carriageway in Ireland. But that was only the beginning for Gallagher and Dillon. They continued to organise and succeeded in getting the Corporation to address the housing problem in the area.

In 1970, Dillon and Gallagher set up the Liberties Festival. It celebrates its fiftieth anniversary this year. It is the longest-running community festival in Dublin. It was set up 'for outsiders, to show people the area's importance in Irish history.' With Dillon and Gallagher at the helm, the festival went from strength to strength, with all manner of events taking place. There was something for everyone, especially the local kids. One thing that they were so aware of was that there weren't that many opportunities for children in the Liberties. Few people in high places were interested in the future of working-class inner-city kids. One of John Gallagher's many legacies is that he set up the Liberties Majorettes in the 1970s, of which I myself was a member, although not very good. The Liberties Majorettes is still going strong today, led by local women, who themselves joined as children. Another initiative by Gallagher was the Dublin Summer Projects. With the help of many local women, gangs of kids would be brought to places like Mosney, Balbriggan, Clara Lara. It was a chance to get them out of the city, run wild and have fun. How they did it I do not know. Marching sometimes forty kids through town to get them on a train out to Balbriggan, and getting us all back again! But we lived for the Summer Projects; they were the highlight of our summer, and we couldn't wait for those two weeks to arrive.

John Gallagher was one of many community activists who were

determined to make sure that the children of the Liberties did not miss out. There was St. Catherine's Girls Club, run by Brother Bernard from Meath Street Church. Every week, girls from all over the Liberties would go to the club. We would play games, do drama—we won the Young Entertainers Award in 1985. And we even got to go to Pwllheli in Wales. If it was traumatic bringing forty girls and boys to Balbriggan for one day, imagine what is was like bringing forty or more girls, ranging from seven to twenty years of age, abroad for a week! But thanks to Brother Bernard and the 'big girls', like Jackie Hunt and Paula Dillon, we all got there and back safely. There was also the children's choir in St. Catherine's Church, which was run by Miss Devine. The choir is still active and, like the majorettes, its leaders are women who joined the choir when they were young girls. And there were just as many activities for the boys in the area. Places like the O.L.V. Club and the St. Catherine's Boys Club were central to giving the boys an outlet for their energy. In a bid to highlight the fact that there were very few sporting or recreational facilities in the area, John Gallagher became involved in the Dublin Inner-City Games. This was at the time that the heroin crisis was gripping Dublin's inner-city. Unfortunately, the Liberties is still lacking in this area. People like John Gallagher, Larry Dillon, Brother Bernard and many others across the city tried to give us kids as many opportunities as possible. What these organisations did was to show us that we mattered, that we could do whatever we wanted if we put our mind to it. They gave us confidence, and one thing they gave us in bucket-loads was pride—pride in ourselves and pride in our community.

I was lucky to have that same experience in school. I went to Presentation Convent, Warrenmount, primary and secondary school. And I have to say I have nothing but fond memories of my schooldays. There has been a long tradition of education in the Liberties. In 1813 the Carmelite nuns ran a school, where Warrenmount is today. At the time, education for poorer children wasn't high on the agenda, especially for girls. The Carmelites changed that and sought to educate the children of the area. When the Carmelites returned to their status as a closed order, Presentation Sisters took up the task in 1892. The school is still going strong today.

I found my teachers at Warrenmount so supportive. If they saw a talent in you they would encourage it. I recently met my teacher from third class while giving a walking tour about revolutionary Irish women. I thanked her for being such a great teacher. Chatting to her gave me a huge insight into her dedication, not just to her profession, but to the children of the Liberties. She had been asked to teach at private schools many times, and each time she refused because she felt her place was in the Liberties, to encourage and educate inner-city kids. It was not something she bragged about; she only told me because I asked her. And in secondary school I had amazing teachers. One that springs to mind was Miss Byrne, my history teacher.

She was so passionate about history you couldn't help but notice. To see the passion that someone had in their work was inspiring. After my dad, it was Miss Byrne who ignited in me my passion for history.

So these are just some of the experiences I had growing up in the Liberties and just some of the people who inspired me. And where am I now? Well, I went to college and studied Classical Animation. Another thing my dad told me was to try your hand at anything. If you fail, so be it, but at least give it a go. So I did.

I loved Irish revolutionary history, I couldn't get enough of it, and I wanted to work in history in some shape or form. Enter John Gallagher once again. John had set up the Nicholas of Myra Heritage Centre in Carman's Hall. It was a Community Employment Scheme and it literally changed my life. The centre was the beating heart of the Liberties. It wasn't just a heritage centre; it was home to the Liberties Majorettes, there were breakfast and homework clubs, meals on wheels for the elderly, bingo, a crèche, a community advice centre and much more. I worked as a local history researcher, and every year we would put on exhibitions about the Liberties, or some aspect of Dublin history. One exhibition on James Joyce won a prestigious UNESCO Award. I went back to college to study Irish history and began tour guiding. My dream job was to be a guide in Kilmainham Gaol. That dream became a reality in 2006. My dad was so proud. And after telling him, the next person I told was John Gallagher. You would think he had won the Lotto; one of his kids had done good.

And it went on from there. I have written six books about the Irish Revolution, worked in RTÉ, have appeared on television and radio documentaries, am a Researcher on RTÉ Radio's The History Show. I lecture on Irish history to American students and do walking tours. I have lectured around the world, and the first thing that I will always say, very proudly, is that I am from the Liberties.

Like those who inspired me, I want to give back. I am a member of the Liberties Cultural Association (LCA). It is a voluntary organisation, set up by James Madigan and Dublin City Council Historian in Residence Cathy Scuffil, two locals. We're a small group, James, Cathy, Kim Olin, Maria O'Reilly, Fran O'Shea and Noel Fleming. We all either live or work in the Liberties and we are passionate about it. Like John Gallagher before us, our aim is to promote the rich heritage of the Liberties.

In recent years the Liberties has seen great change, not all of it for the better. After years of being neglected, suddenly the Liberties was on everyone's radar—gentrification had arrived. While regeneration is welcomed, who it is aimed at and what is being built leaves a lot to be desired. The Liberties has a long history of social housing, as far back as the 1880s. Unfortunately, the focus now, by those who think they know what's best for Dublin city, is to have transient communities. By doing so, the people who have called the Liberties home are being pushed out. The area is dominated by student accommodation and hotels. Where is the balance? We find ourselves in the same position that Larry Dillon and John Gallagher were in all those years ago. That is why the LCA was set up. The Liberties has fewer facilities now than it did ten years ago. The Nicholas of Myra Heritage Centre is gone. The Iveagh Markets, an indoor market built for the traders in the Liberties, lies in ruins. There is no library, no community centre, but we like a challenge.

One initiative the LCA came up with was to do walking tours of the area. Seeing as though we didn't have a venue to do talks, we used the streets. The response from the locals was fantastic. In 2018 James Madigan developed a Shopkeepers Tour of Meath Street. The idea was simple, meet your local butcher, fishmonger, fruit and veg man, shopkeeper, local publican and sample their wares. It was a great success and just so happened to coincide with the arrival of fifty American students who were going to be living in the area in one of the new student complexes. For the four months they lived here, they shopped, socialised, volunteered and really made the Liberties their home. They gave back. We also regularly host events for local schoolchildren, working with the Community Development Officers in DCC. All of which have been a great success. We just want to give the same opportunities that were given to us. In light of our work with the American students, the LCA won a Pride of Place Award, a first for the Liberties.

The Liberties is changing, but that's nothing new. It is because it embraces change that the Liberties has survived. But that change should not come at the cost of the community. Although gentrification is well under way, there are still problems. We shouldn't have to protest to have basic facilities that other areas have. In a recent survey carried out by SICCDA it was found that 43% of adults in the Liberties have a third level education. That's compared to 41% in Dublin and 36% in the Republic of Ireland. The people of the Liberties don't need to be saved; they need to be listened to. They are trying to rebrand the Liberties. It is hip, it is trendy, it's a great place to live. But the people of the Liberties already knew that. I knew it from my earliest years.

So that is my story, my experience of growing up in a working-class community in Dublin. Those wise words from my dad, 'Be proud of where you come from' are always with me. I am testament that you don't have to live up to the label others put on you because of where you are from, and I am one of many. It is my badge of honour, and I wouldn't have it any other way.

P.S.

We never ate our young in the Liberties.

Anita Gracey

was born in West Belfast when internment was introduced and she hasn't left! Anita's writings are influenced by being a wheelchair user, current affairs and her working-class background.

Anita has been published in *Poetry Ireland Review, Washing Windows—Irish Women Write Poetry* (ed. Eavan Boland), *North Star* (ed. Woman Aloud), *Abridged, The Poets Republic, The Honest Ulsterman, Poetry NI, The Blue Nib, Culture Matters, Sonder, Domestic Violence Anthology, CAP Anthologies, Bangor Literary Review, Sonder*and *Pandemic*. Her work has featured in *The Poetry Jukebox*. She was shortlisted Over the Edge New Writer of the Year 2018, longlisted for the Hennessy New Irish Writing in 2019 and shortlisted Chultúrlann Poetry Competition 2020.

Anita is supported by an iDA award, managed by the University of Atypical on behalf of the Arts Council of Northern Ireland.

Sketch of an Atheist

In memory of Brian Gracey 1965-2020

Stars hung from the night sky when my brother was castaway, bones lost in pj top, his pallor a dismal grey. No more savage sweep of the eyes, the kingfisher flash of blue. We parted during lockdown, a time which was appropriate for you.

I remember he had chosen for his confirmation name the saintly 'Spiderman'; the priest would not allow it—God mustn't be a fan. An annoyed teacher wrote about it to mummy. Maybe this is the moment when he and God parted company.

On caravan holidays he would tell tales of chemical loo axemen. Men with earwig savagery who would eat me like I was a strawberry. Terrified, I clung to teddy; I was gullible then.

Petrol bombs and riots were nothing to him in his small world—so unpretty, but he was innocent then, he shook it off like Belfast confetti. He didn't see God on the street much, in a childhood marked with barbed violence. Armed with parents' love, he survived his teens and the experience.

God surely wouldn't dole out disability to him with Spiderman's invincibility! But two long legs became four wheels; he'd shrug saying what can you do, you put up with it, he had to. He took pride in his independence as a man of wheels, and was stubborn, a warrior strength revealed.

He got top marks in horticulture at college, but he had no real interest. Leaves shiver their neglect, soil in need of a drink, and his meagre plastic plants scream 'reject'. He refused to take root and travelled abroad to reboot. His photos were of sunny trips, anchoring girls to him, long arms around shoulders, adrift with his manic grin. God's gift to the ladies he thought he was, well you gotta love a tryer was his self-applause.

Now, living in a flat, he preferred to call it an apartment; for new friends he created a whole new backstory, papered in gilt parchment.

For his funeral he didn't want a fuss, no prayers nor lament, no winged angels playing—he didn't believe in heavenly ascent. The wake was three hours in the car park, greeting family and friends. Two at a time to view the closed coffin, a very surreal bend.

The funeral was restricted to ten people, with social distancing spaced apart. We filled the space with his stories, talking from the heart. His brothers wanted to carry the coffin, but this was not his fate. So, the cars followed the hearse, and we were turned away from the crematorium gate.

As an atheist Brian believed he would not be in the sunset, or the morning birdsong, or the clinging dewdrop; for him that would be wrong.

Rachael Hegarty

was born the seventh child of a seventh child in Dublin, and reared in the working-class neighbourhood of Finglas. Widely published and broadcast, her debut collection, *Flight Paths over Finglas*, won the 2018 Shine Strong Award. Her second collection, *May Day 1974*, was launched on 17 May to commemorate the Dublin and Monaghan bombings. Rachael contributed to *The Children of the Nation: An Anthology of Working People's Poetry from Contemporary Ireland* and was shortlisted for the Francis MacManus and the New Irish writing in prose. Her kids say she is a doctor with dyslexia and uses the F word way too much: Finglas, feminism and feckin' poetry.

The Dodgy Box

Debbie held the piece of paper with the address on it in her hand. The walk between the Artane and Darndale roundabouts was longer than she had reckoned. A hot August day; the air was close and her hands were sweating loads. Her day off; by rights she should be taking a paddle in the waves at Dollymount. But no, here she was making her way to one of the dodgier estates to buy a dodgy box from a cousin of the yonfella in the warehouse. She felt the piece of paper in her fist. It was limp with her sweat. She stuffed the small square of paper into her side pocket. No worries, she'd remember the address: 14 Bluebell Avenue.

Bluebell Avenue, Jaysus knows when this place last saw bluebells. All Debbie could see were grey paths and tarmac roads. There must be some muppet in the Corpo with a weird sense of humour. The more ropey the neighbourhood the more poetic the names: Murphy's Barn, Apple Orchard —they made it sound like a day out in the country, when really, they were just good places for scoring gear. The poetic place names and the height of the speed bumps were a bit of a giveaway. Speed bumps so high they could do as much damage to a car as the spikes from a Garda stinger. Mad high speedbumps and poetic place names equals one interesting neighbourhood. Debbie would tell them tell-tale signs to her kids if they were ever in a position to afford to go looking for a place of their own. Chance would be a fine thing.

The heat was killing. She wished she hadn't worn jeans, but her second eldest had said she'd looked like a muppet in a sundress. And now, even she saw the sense in not looking like a muppet in this estate. Some of the houses had iron shutters over the windows and front doors. Debbie wondered what kind of anti-social behaviour could get a family kicked out of here. And where were they putting them? The local authorities were the most anti-social of them all—throwing families out on the road and into the hell of homeless services. One good thing about this pandemic—no more evictions.

People talked of the second wave. People talked of a hard lockdown.

People talked of how the pandemic would make the winter longer, would make the winter harder. But all Debbie wanted was a dodgy box. There was no way they could get through a winter lockdown and them having nothing to do but watch the free TV. Sweating or not the sunny weather made for an easier lockdown. Christ, if it had of been one of those wet miserable summers and a global pandemic, there would have been people leaping into the Liffey in droves. Debbie needed this dodgy box for her family's sanity. Two adults, three teens and two kids would need all the channels they could get. Covid-19 was shite. Debbie could use as much digital distraction as possible. Cost was a factor. A dodgy box was the answer.

Himself did not like the idea of the dodgy box. But it wasn't him the kids came running to with their whinging and moaning about the lack of channels. Besides, Debbie had done the sums. With her wages from the supermarket and his pandemic payment they could barely make ends meet as it was. And it's not like she didn't know how to economize. Two decades on the tills was like having a master's degree in economics. Debbie knew the cheap cuts of meat to buy, the quality own brands to get, and how to switch from cereals to porridge, in order to save a few bob. She'd have to tighten the purse strings even tighter when his pandemic payment stopped. Well, thought Debbie, what the husband doesn't know, won't harm him.

The husband had worked as a night porter for seventeen years. Long hours but good enough wages and the perks of good hotel rates when they took the kids away for a midweek special. But the hotel industry was in a heap now. The husband still talked of going back, but in her heart of hearts she knew all that crowd in hospitality were fucked. That meant a lot of jobs gone from their estate. All those receptionists, kitchen porters, cleaners, bar staff, waitresses and waiters—the whole bleedin' lot, getting the pandemic payment. And who knows for how long before they'd be drawing the labour and trying to live on even less.

Where was this bleedin' house? How big was this estate? Debbie wanted to take her phone out and use the map thingy, but the kids had her well warned of bike boys who reefed the phones outta aulwans' hands. She cursed herself for not mapping out a route beforehand.

Debbie felt someone staring at her. A man sitting on a front wall, looking her up and down, pullin' on a smoke like his life depended on it and wondering what she was doing on his road. He looked the same age as herself, early forties. Or maybe early thirties, hard to tell, rough living could add a good decade onto a face. She gave him a nod, didn't smile and jutted out her shoulder like she didn't give a shite. She felt a tear of sweat run down the centre of her back. Your man stood up and walked back towards his front door.

Suddenly Debbie wished she had told her husband she was going off to buy a dodgy box. She wished there was no pandemic. She wished she didn't have to keep her kids in, hopefully, watching 600 channels and not getting the virus. She wanted none of hers to get the virus. She needed this dodgy box. She kept going.

She searched around for door numbers. She had seen a number 3 a few houses back. But she hadn't seen any other numbers since. She wondered if the houses were odds on one side and evens on the other, but she could not see that far across the road. She needed glasses. She really needed glasses. Colette at work said the PRSI would get you a free eye test. She needed to make an appointment. Were they taking appointments? Covid-19, maybe not?

She heard shouting: a man and a woman. She couldn't make out the words, but the man's tone was gruff and the woman barked back. Gave as good as she got. Debbie just needed to find house number 14, get the dodgy box and get off this estate before the off-licences opened up. She knew from her old neighbourhood in Finglas, once gargle was thrown into the equation, well, things would only get messier.

And there it was, number 14, a nice house with a cobblelocked driveway and a 202 Lexus parked outside. Johno from the warehouse had said his uncle, Gitzer, was a bit rough around the edges, but he did a great line of dodgy boxes. Things must be good in the dodgy box business. She took her phone out and sent a text message to Gitzer—the new normal, no knocking on doors or touching doorbells during the pandemic. She heard the text go through and waited outside. She stared at the front door. It had well-polished glass. Someone in there must be very house proud. Debbie wondered if there was a Mrs Gitzer and did they have many kids? And if they did, how come their kids didn't manky up the glass at their front door?

The door opened and a yonfella walked out. He looked around seventeen or eighteen, dirty blond hair and a blue North Face tracksuit. Debbie's eldest lad had saved a three weeks' worth of lawn-mowing money to buy one.

'Story?' The boy tilted his head, shimmied by the car and came down the drive towards Debbie. He kept the two-metre distance.

'Hiya, I'm Debbie. Johno sent me. Maybe I could have a word with your Dad?' She felt like a bit of an ejit; she didn't know if this kid knew about the sideline business operating out of his gaff.

'Me Da? No, I don't think so,' the yonfella shrugged his shoulders. 'Last I heard he went out for a bottle of milk and never came back.'

'Right.' Debbie felt a redner start to creep up from her neck and onto her face. Scarlet.

'I'll be off so.' She was going to strangle Johno when she got her hands on him.

'Only messing with you Mrs.' The yonfella's face broadened into a smile. 'I'm Gitzer, Johnno told me you'd be stalling by.'

'Ah sorry.' Debbie was confused. 'The whole uncle thing, I thought you'd be older'.

'Big families.' Gitzer smiled. 'You know yourself.'

'Yes.' Debbie would figure out the family tree later, but for now she reached into her pocket. She handed over that wad of five twenty euro notes. And Gitzer pulled out a Lidl bag from the boot of the Lexus. She looked inside. The box was about a third of the size of a DVD player. Debbie wondered how she was gonna work it. 'Thanks.'

'Christopher,' a woman called out from the front door, 'would you bring that lady in and not be doing your business in the middle of the street for the world and his wife to see.' The woman had dirty blonde hair and was wearing a sundress. Evidently, Christopher didn't mind if his Ma looked like a muppet.

'You're grand.' Debbie didn't want this yonfella to be getting grief from his Ma.

'It's not grand.' The woman folded her arms. 'Besides, Mrs, I'm not being funny, but you look melted, where are you after walking from?'

'Artane.' Debbie wondered if she should have told them where she was from and all. The sweat was running down her back now.

'Ma.' Gitzer pocketed the money. 'Sure, we're all done here.'

'Good.' His Ma pointed towards the Lexus. 'You can give this woman a lift home, it's too hot for walking, the buses are crawling with the virus and sure most won't stop in anyways.'

His Ma wagged his finger at him. 'Just mind you keep all the windows rolled down. No offence Mrs.' With that his Ma closed the front door.

'Come on so.' The locks on the car clunked and Gitzer opened the driver's door.

'This is your car?' Debbie couldn't disguise her surprise. Gitzer looked like he made his confo a couple of years back, not be minding having a licence to drive such a mad dear car. Debbie looked at his face. Part of his jaw line still had that peachy fuzz of teenage lads—not even stubble. 'Ah, here, do you even have a licence?' Debbie felt a bit braver. If this fella was still listening to his Ma then he might listen to other aulwans too.

'Ah now, it's bad enough I have to take shite from her.' Gitzer opened the passenger door for Debbie. 'Please get in, or she'll be at me for the rest of the day and banging on about respecting women, respecting me elders, blah, blah, blah...' He started up the engine and reversed out. 'Besides, you're a workmate of Johno's. I'll install the box for free and show you how it works.'

'Ok.' Debbie sat in, felt the white leather seat and wondered what she'd tell the husband. Fuck it—he'd see the sense of it. Besides, the hubby would love them history channels. He was mad for all that history malarkey. Debbie just hoped he'd be alright with her rocking home with a randomer. Sure, wasn't Gitzer Johno's uncle? Wasn't he a nice lad with a nice Ma? Alright his little business enterprise wasn't 100% legit, but sure what business was? Gitzer was going to help Debbie sort out the gizmo and then her family would have great telly for the winter lockdown.

They drove down Bluebell Avenue. Gitzer put on the air conditioning. Lovely, cold air flooded the car. Debbie felt the weight of the dodgy box on her lap and held on to it with two hands.

Kevin Higgins

was born in London of Irish parents, grew up in Galway and lived in London again during his twenties. He has lived back in Galway City for the past twenty-five years. He has worked variously as a petrol pump attendant, an accounts clerk, a deliverer of flyers for a North London mini-cab company, and Education Officer at Galway Centre for the Unemployed. He was also for many years an activist and was Chair of Enfield Against The Poll Tax in London in the early 1990s. Since 2003 he has made his living as a creative writing tutor and poetry workshop facilitator. Kevin's poems have been quoted in *The Daily Telegraph, The Independent, The Times* (London), *Hot Press* magazine, *The Daily Mirror* and on *The Vincent Browne Show*, and read aloud by Ken Loach at a political meeting in London.

Vigil in support of Irish Water during Seanad vote on Wednesday

Economist Dan O'Brien and distinguished University of Limerick academic Peadar Kirby have come together to organise a vigil in support of Irish Water, which will take place this Wednesday, December 17th, from 6 p.m. outside the gates of Leinster House. The vigil is timed to coincide with the Seanad's vote on the Irish Water bill.

In a joint statement issued last night, O'Brien and Kirby said:

It has become clear to us that there is a serious danger that the Irish Water bill could be defeated in the Seanad on Wednesday. In normal circumstances this would only force a delay of three months. But, given all that has happened, such a delay might prove terminal. We have come together to call on the Irish people to assemble at the gates of our national parliament to help soften the spines of those few wavering Senators, more than a few of whom we have met personally at dinner parties. If this Bill is defeated in the Seanad it could lead to the collapse of Irish Water, which would represent a huge victory for the forces of uncouthness and general smelliness. We feel it's time bald economists and academics came together and united against our common enemy. We have nothing to lose but our immense opinion of ourselves.

Speakers will include Senator Ivana Bacik, Kathy Sheridan of *The Irish Times,* and Fionnán Sheahan of *The Irish Independent* who has vowed to turn up wearing underpants made exclusively from the hair of Denis O'Brien.

It is also hoped that Clarence Thomas of the US Supreme Court will be in attendance and speak at the event, as communications consultant Terry Prone has advised the organisers that it's always handy to have a black guy on board to soften the image, when you're trying to set up something

79

like Irish Water.

There will also be, we hope, ecumenical prayers led by some Church of Ireland bishop or other. If anyone knows any such bishops, or even someone who's prepared to spend the evening pretending to be a vicar, give us a call on 1890 448 448. We'd be happy to slip such a 'vicar' a few euros and maybe set him up with a nice girl for afterwards.

(blog post, December 14th 2014)

Jennifer Horgan

was born in Cork, Ireland, and spent twelve years in London and Abu Dhabi. She is a teacher and has experienced great privilege. However, living abroad heightened her awareness of that privilege and she is interested in exploring inequality in local and global settings. She returned home in 2018 to work in Cork Educate Together Secondary School. She has had work accepted for publication in *Crossways* magazine, *Idler, Euonia Review, Nine Muses, Blue Nib, Culture Matters—An Anthology of Contemporary Irish Poetry, Honest Ulsterman, The Irish Examiner* and the *Evening Echo*. She is currently working on a non-fiction title with Orpen Press.

Their Daughter's Bib

Her death should never have happened. Of that, everyone is certain, especially Orla. But it still doesn't make her feel any more responsible.

She guides herself back (ever so gently) to a few days before.

She, Orla, is watching her daughter struggle to breathe—choking—and is struck by the fact that she is doing absolutely nothing about it. She sits, watching, waiting to see how the scene unfolds, taking a mental note of how strikingly familiar her child's colour is, the exact pink of the desert flowers surrounding their three floor villa. Maeve, like her mother, is a perfect example of your typical Irish. Her skin reflecting Ireland's landscape, usually grey and with a general blueness, borrowed maybe from the heavy, bulging veins of their starved ancestors.

Maeve's eyes are screaming blue now, electrified and watering. Her bib is blue too, stained orange by the dinner she's choking on.

It's somewhere in this moment that Orla has a profound thought: that there is something wrong with her. Something very wrong, that she should sit here, as her daughter chokes, presumably towards death. But more than this, that there is something very wrong with her world and all the people in it, with the men and the women and all the things they spend their time creating, the houses and the cars and appliances. Something strange and wrong with the world they have made, that she should sit here watching her child, now turning purple, doing absolutely nothing.

In the next moment, the maid is there and she has the child on her knee, banging her back before reaching her fingers down her throat and scooping out the offending morsel. She's very glad that her daughter seems better now. Her truculent roar dulled to a high-pitched whine. It seems the first aid course for maids she'd sent Lisa on served its function, after all.

She would be sure to lord that over Eoin.

She watches silently as the maid moves about the kitchen, removing the child's bib and washing it down before placing it in the washing machine. Her busyness makes Orla feel even more frozen, pointless in her own home, with her own kids. There's something very real about that pointless feeling. Here, nothing really belongs to anyone, anyone other than the locals that is. It's a rented world, a huge air-conditioned palace that'll kick you out the second you hit sixty. Your feelings for the place count for nothing. There are no old white faces here, no old people from India or Sri Lanka. Those faces disappear, fade out off-stage somewhere else to tell their stories. But she knows they won't leave before they have to. Abu Dhabi is home now and their friends are their family. Retirement will be a kind of death, she supposes, when she bothers to think of it at all.

And, of course, there's the money. Leaving simply isn't an option.

***

Later that evening, Orla remembers this moment her daughter nearly dies, while Sharon jabbers on about the importance of play-based learning; she's a teacher, too, and a far more devoted one.

—It's not good enough Orls. This shit should be coming up in Head of Year meetings and it's clearly not. They're probably too busy comparing the size of their egos. Useless the lot of them.

—Ya, you're right. It's certainly happening in the UK.

Orla orders another round of free prosecco. She pretends she's from the UK now. It's easier that way. Her British colleagues barely know Ireland's a separate country, and she's tired of explaining that she doesn't actually go home to Britain in the summer. She's increasingly distracted by Sharon's thread veins tonight, and how she really isn't making a very effective effort to hide them. Thread veins and facial hair spoil the easy glamour of Ladies' night. Sharon should know better. The reality of their ageing imperfections dampens this weekly euphoria—of not paying a single dirham for fancy drinks and a five-star bathroom experience.

—This is the good shit, isn't it? Not like that skanky stuff in the Shangri La last week.

Sharon is beside herself with smugness. She's the one who decides where they're going. Sharon spends most weekdays compiling hit lists, best deals, most stunning spots, most attentive waiting staff. Hotels without bathroom servants are preferred. No-one needs to be handed paper to dry their hands; that much they can manage themselves. Her high standards strike Orla as slightly ironic, considering she's a cheapskate looking for a bargain in a bargain bin dress from that shop upstairs in Khalidiyah Mall. She even makes a point of only bringing a credit card so Orla has to pay for the cab every time. She's a good gossip, though, and that's important when you're living in a parched and lonely ex-pat bubble. The one thing you need is something or, even better, someone to talk about.

—Did you hear about the science teacher in secondary? He's been having it off with the coach's wife. Poor guy doesn't have a clue. This is going to explode!

Sharon is jittery with the excitement of something actually happening in their world. Orla often imagines friends back home seeing her in places like these. God, they'd kill to even dip their toe in this pool of luxury. But Orla also knows that she would have far more fun if she was here with those Irish friends. They'd probably stay out longer too, might even stretch to buying a round once the freebie hours dried up. No doubt they'd get a great kick out of chatting to a few lads out on the pull.

Most nights, Orla and Sharon only speak to each other. If anyone tries to approach them, they assume the worst; they have come to think of themselves as prizes in a contest most people can't afford. They usually leave just as the wave of eligible men darken the beachside bars, lights flashing and music blaring across the calm waters of a very still and salty sea.

How clever they should feel, leaving the men so thirsty, so unsatisfied. Men who pay for their drink of course—their only treat is to look at women. Women like Orla, who look after themselves, who smell like they look after themselves. Only once did she get in trouble, when an Indian jumped into a lift and rubbed himself up against her. She rarely thinks of it.

Leaving the taxi, stretching to a five dirham tip because he hasn't attempted a conversation, Orla feels entirely normal. It's only when Orla wakes in the night—that she starts to think something might be happening. Inside her. Something that feels close to breaking, like the way she used to feel as a child in her swimming suit, too skinny, too pale, lacking in some way, foolish.

Did she forget to feed the cat? Maybe.

They have a cat of sorts. A street cat they never allow inside the apartment, one the children, mostly Orla, feed in the promise they might one day earn a dog. Orla reminds herself often that this cat would be dead without her, so covered in sores and malnourished when it first appeared, squealing at their doorway. She feels endlessly good about it.

First checking that her phone is still charging, she turns the other way towards her husband, breathing in and resenting his sour meaty smell on their freshly laundered linen. The air conditioning rattles slightly. She closes her eyes and imagines the sound is of a train. She's standing on a misty platform, waiting to be taken somewhere else. Somewhere cool and forgiving.

***

The maid is unusually dour the next morning. She is generally a convenient kind of absent. There in body only, her hair being pushed violently over her eyes by little hands as she battles to fasten Orla's children's school shirts and shoes. Orla, busy down the hall, applying fake tan or locating a rogue earring.

But today there's a definite sullenness. Orla knows Lisa wants her to ask why, so of course she doesn't. She has too much on, packing for the day, work, gym and finding the kids' library books, that they have never once managed to read in time.

She is too busy to play Lisa's juvenile games.

She knows Lisa has never liked or trusted her. And Orla resents that Lisa does little to hide it. Other maids she meets in her friends' houses practically interrupt their coffee mornings to extol the virtues of their madam. Not Lisa. Lisa looks like she's been smacked in the face with her wet mop most of the time. Or that she's just discovered an infestation of cockroaches in the study. Which she did to be fair, but they're long gone. As is Orla's patience with her mood swings. Lisa gets a lot of perks. They always pay her for babysitting extra hours and they give her the full two day weekend. Sharon thinks she's crazy for that, and Orla knows she could change her mind any minute; it's not like Lisa would leave her, break her visa and head back to where she came from. Not a chance.

She leaves without a goodbye and arrives home ten hours later to find Lisa and Eoin in a conspiratorial huddle in the kitchen.

There's no fear of anything sexual here. God no, the thought alone makes Orla giggle. Lisa is about four foot and Eoin is over six foot. They are not only from different countries, they're bloody different species. But Eoin is a soft touch and the maid knows it.

By the time she has checked on the kids, Lisa is gone, but a heavy urgency hangs around Eoin's annoyingly slumped body, just about keeping itself upright on the stool. He's put on weight since coming here and is starting to grow that awful jowl around his neck his dad has. It changes his entire face, changes the deal. His eyes are getting smaller too, sinking into his expanding face, like gerbil eyes, or something dark and pointless. As irritating as the way he chews, lathering up extra saliva in his cheeks just to annoy her.

He's flicking through photographs Lisa sent of their baby during the day. Maeve is wearing the same blue bib, immaculately clean, blanched by the dry heat of the balconies. She could never accuse Lisa of inefficiency.

—Lisa is upset. With you. With us. With the way she's being treated. She told me what happened the other morning with Maeve. That you didn't even say thank you.

While he's speaking, Orla reaches for the cool glass of white wine Eoin has been enjoying with his meal, no doubt poured by Lisa and chilled before he arrived home in an effort to get him onside. She takes a long, slow gulp.

—Did I not? Orla feigns. I think I was in shock.

Eoin says nothing for longer than is reasonable.

84

—She wants an advance of the next four months. Says her mother needs some operation in Manila. She needs it quickly and then she'll be ok. What do you think?

Orla feels a glut of rage in her stomach. It is ugly and bilious. She manages a vague shrug, willing Eoin to say something more, to steer them in a direction. She goes for her own glass and to the fridge, pulls out the open bottle of Oyster Bay.

—I suppose we should, Eoin continues obediently.

—It's not like she can go anywhere, unless she wants to leave the country that is. And she has a point. She saved our daughter's life for fuck's sake. I suppose it's the least we can do.

Orla wants to smash the bottle over his irritatingly balding head. She imagines his broad, tanned forehead with a shock of blood, like a defeated Macbeth in some modern ex-pat drama.

—Only because we paid for the training; only because we provide her with a decent living. Do you know that her house in the Philippines is twice, three times the size of our manky little two-up two-down in Dublin?

The incomparability of the two homes strikes them both at that moment, as does their ugliness. Orla says nothing more, takes her wine to bed and has absolutely no desire to do anything but sleep.

Eoin mutters that he will take care of it and the next morning he does. Lisa's face returns to the usual uplipped scowl, without the accompanying cloud of gloom. Orla hates her for all of it; she hates herself and Eoin too. But she still refuses to thank Lisa for anything.

That is why when Lisa calls, in hysterics at nine o'clock that night, Orla can only listen between gasps. Not a single word comes to her. Not a single thought, profound or otherwise. Orla passes the phone to Eoin, saying only

—Her mother's died.

There is barely a minute before Orla thinks of the cost of the flight she'll be needing and how that advance should cover it adequately. Again, she leaves it to Eoin and goes to check on her three growing children, cool and satisfied in their air-conditioned beds.

That night, the pink flowers continue to bloom outside their villa gate. The tawny cat moves territorially about their bushes. Orla begins to plan the next couple of weeks without help, feeling almost relieved that they will have to manage for a bit on their own. It is comforting to feel that way; it's comforting to feel anything.

***

Paul Jeffcutt

His father worked in a factory and his mother worked in an office. Paul went to technical school, but became the first member of his extended family to go to university. He began writing in his spare time.

His second collection of poetry, *The Skylark's Call*, is published by Dempsey & Windle (2020). His debut collection, *Latch*, was with Lagan Press (2010). Paul has won thirty-three awards for poetry in national and international competitions. His poems have been published in Australia, Austria, Canada, Ireland, the UK and the USA.

In 2011 Paul began a weekly blog, *Writing to Survive*, about his cancer treatment and living with the threat of recurrence. Over time the blog has been extended into related concerns. Paul's blog has garnered many plaudits and has hundreds of regular readers.

He lives in County Down, Northern Ireland. www.pauljeffcutt.net

'Sixteen Tons'

I began to pee blood and went to casualty. They found a tumour which had taken over my left kidney and had grown most of the way to my heart. After a big operation to remove the tumour and my kidney, I was given a surveillance scan every six months. For three years these scans had found no evidence of the cancer returning.

Whenever my scan came around, my wife and I would be filled with dread. The worst time was waiting for the results. After several weeks of sleepless nights, we would be called in to the Cancer Centre to meet my oncologist and hear the verdict.

'The scan shows a small lump in your liver,' announced the oncologist.

I swallowed hard and glanced towards my wife. She winced and squeezed my hand.

'It could be a capsular deposit or a metastasis,' he continued.

I stared quizzically at him.

'A metastasis is a tumour that has appeared in another part of your body,' he said.

I nodded, blankly, my mind reverberating with awful images of hospital and operations.

'So I'm sending you for an urgent MRI scan,' he said.

A worried week later, we returned to the Cancer Centre. Attending the MRI suite, I first had to fill in a questionnaire. They wanted to know whether I had any metal in my body. I could safely say no to the questions about body piercings and shrapnel wounds, but I declared the sternal wires and surgical clips from my previous surgery.

We sat side-by-side in the waiting room, holding hands. Alone in our thoughts, we hardly spoke. When my name was called by the nurse, my wife kissed me and gave me a hug.

In the cubicle, I took off my clothes, then my watch and bracelet and put on the grey hospital gown. I sat on the bench and waited; underneath I was naked apart from my pants. A knock on the door and I was called in for the scan.

The MRI scanner is a long slim tunnel surrounded by a huge magnet. I lay on the narrow bed in front of the machine. A curved panel was strapped around my midriff. Then headphones were put on me.

Because MRI scanners are very noisy, the radiographer speaks to you through the headphones. But most of the time music is playing very loudly.

Move closer...

I began to slide into the scanner feet first.

Move your body real close...

I was right inside the scanner, its grey walls just a few inches away.

Feels like we're really making love...

I was entombed. The scan started and loud pulses roared around me. My midriff began to get warm. I longed for my wife, but, despite the entreaties of Phyllis Nelson, I wasn't feeling like making love.

'Hold your breath,' said the radiographer. And the pulses began again. They sounded like a deep thumping siren.

People say a man is made out of mud.

A poor man's made out of muscle and blood...

Again I was told to hold my breath. The pulsing reverberated around me.

You load sixteen tons and what do you get?

Another day older and deeper in debt...

I was trapped, as if I was at the bottom of a coalmine. Tennessee Ernie Ford boomed on as I panted, allowed to breathe again.

St. Peter don't you call me, because I can't go

I owe my soul to the company store.

I was hoping against hope that the lump was nothing serious. But, for the most part, I was already convinced that the cancer had returned. I didn't know for sure, of course. But I did know that there would be plenty more sleepless nights before we'd actually find out. And then what?

I pictured my wife in the room next door, anxiously waiting for me. She would be doing her best to remain calm. And here I was, stuck in this tunnel of fear.

When the night has come

And the land is dark

And the moon is the only light we'll see.

'Nearly finished,' said the radiographer, cheerfully. 'You alright?'

I didn't answer. I was listening to Sam Cooke.
No, I won't be afraid
Oh, I won't be afraid
Just as long as you stand
Stand by me.

Rosemary Jenkinson

is PULP—Protestant Unionist/Loyalist Poor. She lives in Willowfield in inner-city East Belfast and has worked with local communities and groups of ex-prisoners on plays and other writing projects. Rosemary has lived in working-class areas of the UK such as Dundee, Gateshead, Gillingham and Brixton. As a playwright, her plays often focus on paramilitarism and street culture: *The Bonefire, Johnny Meister + The Stitch, Wonderwall, The Lemon Tree, Basra Boy, Cuchullain, Stella Morgan* and *A Midsummer Night's Riot.* She writes political satires (*Michelle and Arlene*) and plays about social issues: *Lives in Translation* centres on Somali asylum seekers; *May the Road Rise Up* deals with homelessness. Essays for *The Irish Times* have explored identity and women's writing. She is also a short story writer and her stories feature outsiders on the margins of society. Her latest book of short stories is *Lifestyle Choice 10mgs* (Doire Press).

This Year is Cancelled

Lockdown Musings from Belfast
29/05/2020

I've always thought pandemics were a thing of the past, although as a keen reader I grew up immersed in the romance of such diseases wantonly destroying youth. In one of my childhood books *Anne of the Island,* Ruby Gillis, the school beauty, finds her one true love and promptly dies of 'galloping consumption' as TB was known. Fortunately, TB is rare nowadays, and if you die of such a thing as consumption it would no doubt be obesity-related!

I wonder if I've had, or will have, Covid-19? The insidious thing about this disease is that it ranges from asymptomatic to deadly. Back in March, I overheard receptionists at my local surgery fielding constant calls from elderly patients worried about their coughs. 'Are you sure it wasn't a wee bit of dust in your throat when you were drinking your tea?' one receptionist asked, clearly used to batting away paranoia.

Given that we're led by a serial inseminator who can't even plan far enough ahead in his sex life to use a condom (yes, I am alluding to his ex-lover's alleged abortions), planning for the outbreak was never going to go well. The actual announcement of lockdown came as a shock. 'From this evening... you must stay at home,' said Boris, and there was a hectic beating from inside my heart like a winged animal trying to escape. My eyes went wet at the enormity of the changes to our lives.

Who could have dreamt that our social contact would shrink to the point of waving to relatives through windows? The whole notion has a fairy tale quality to it, like Snow White in a glass coffin or Tilda Swinton sleeping in a glass box. And what about the government directives to sing for twenty seconds while we wash our hands—what are we in, some National Theatre 'soap' opera? Excuse the pun, but it suits the pundemic since everything is ludicrously surreal. To think the year started with an appeal for Big Ben to chime for Brexit and ended up with tolling bells.

Even our language has changed completely. The phrase 'to bump into someone' is no longer relevant. Existent words have reemerged with specific new meanings like 'shielding', 'cocooning', 'self-isolating', 'superspreading' and the definitions are as confusing as government advice. The one positive is that I'm becoming less concerned about superspreader shedders and more worried about developing a toothache since all the dentists are closed. Even a chocolate bar is dangerous these days.

It's hard now to recall what days were like BC Before Coronavirus but I keep running this parallel life in my head, visualizing myself travelling this June with the piquancy of what could have been. It's eerie to walk through the streets and see old posters on the lamp posts and telephone boxes, advertising shows at the end of March. It's as if time stopped at that moment, as if the apocalypse arrived. Luckily, through the darkness, there have been sights and sounds to raise the spirits. In the evenings I can hear street bingo being called out on a PA system to families sitting in their front gardens. I've also had fun with friends betting on when the lockdown would be lifted, but then of course we argued over the actual definition of lockdown release. Did we mean full or partial (a bit like a Brazilian)? At least we can laugh and, to quote Sean O'Casey, 'that's the Irish all over—they treat a joke as a serious thing and a serious thing as a joke'.

We need society to reopen fully. We in Northern Ireland know what it's like to have a war-torn economy blighted by bomb scares and roadblocks, and it had an impact on all of us, affecting our mental health and sapping our energy. It's worth bearing in mind that both the Spanish Flu and the only other plague I've read about, the Great Plague of London, lasted two years each, but there are enough doomladen soothsayers around without me adding to them. I prefer hope.

Having said that, I have witnessed pure desperation. In April, I passed an agitated man in a nearby street knocking on a Catholic priest's door. He asked for money, explaining that he'd lost his job due to coronavirus. The elderly priest was using the door as a shield, obviously scared of infection, and turned him away. I could hear the man cursing as he left.

'Jesus gave to the fucking lepers,' he was crying out, 'but you won't fucking give to me!'

My own personal indigence is due to closed theatres, literary festivals and publishing companies, but I've been able to apply for Arts Council of Northern Ireland artists emergency funding and a self-employed grant. I've never regarded myself as a dilettante, privileged writer. Sometimes in writing we talk about craft, but craft is only one component. To me, I'm in the construction industry and I'm a builder, building stories which will last much longer than those jerry-built social housing flats at the end of my street, erected by greedy constructors. I write in my ex-shipyard worker's parlour house, so I'm part of a working tradition. Of course, it's a modern inner-city street too, and last year the police raided a neighbouring house which Lithuanians had converted into a crystal meth lab. Could we not have a street-lab that does something useful like invent a Covid-19 vaccine?

The solitude of lockdown, combined with extraordinary circumstances means that this is the perfect time to be a writer. It also transpires that reading books is one of the safest things you can do. A study in *The Lancet* said coronavirus can live three days on hard surfaces and three hours on paper, so goodbye Kindle and technology and let's go retro. It's time to record, not to retreat, and even if it's hard to convey these strange times, it's worth trying to capture. L.M. Montgomery who wrote about Ruby Gillis said, 'Next to trying and winning, the best thing is trying and failing'.

Camillus John

was bored and braised in Ballyfermot, a working-class suburb of Dublin, and still lives there to this day. He considers himself working class and always will. His Ma and Da both worked in the rag trade as a sewer and a pattern cutter respectively. He has had fiction published in *The Stinging Fly*, *RTÉ Ten* and *The Lonely Crowd* amongst other organs. He would also like to mention that St. Pats won the FAI cup in 2014 after 53 miserable years of not winning it.

The Rise and Fall of Cinderella's Left Testicle

I'd been sacked. The recession and the new *Lazy Scumbag* legislation were coming after and at me with a vengeance. It was my last day in the job and Alan Purple called me into his office.

'You start as a cleaner in a Blackrock mansion on Monday, Cynthia. I just got the governmental email.'

He pushed the print-out over to me. I read it and nearly wept.

I said, 'This can't be right, Alan. Look at the hours. Six twelve-hour shifts a week. And I'm on call for the remaining twelve as well. Are those intern hours? Surely not?'

'It's not up to me, Cynthia, I didn't enact the legislation myself.'

'I know that, Alan, but it says here that my day off will be either on a Monday or a Tuesday. I won't be able to play the Pigeon Club of a Friday night any more with my band, Cinderella's Left Testicle. Fucking hell, Alan, this is shit.'

Of course, I knew that this would set him off choking on his own disgust and white-foaming at the mouth, but I didn't really care at this stage. My life was drowning and I wanted to lash out while there was still air in my lungs. His face had nearly turned as purple as his surname, and he banged a fist three times down upon his desk, before he spoke at me in his usual manner.

'There's no need for that type of language, Cynthia. No need at all. You remind me of those people I saw in your Ballyfermot, in front of the Gala, selling their wares. They spoke like you as well, funnily enough. And they all seemed dead to me. Dead in the head. What makes them like that, Cynthia? What is it that brings people down to such an unimaginative level of being?'

He wasn't my boss any more, from five o'clock that evening I was officially sacked. I didn't have to hold my tongue around him and his precious easily-offended values anymore. Didn't have to pretend. In a way, I was free to say what I liked. Anyway, that's how my mind was working at the time.

I said, 'You can't say that. You can't say that everyone is the same and tar them all with the one brush.'

'Well, I am saying it, Cynthia. Forget political correctness—they're all dead in that place, Ballyfermot. Brain dead and lazy scroungers.'

He'd never said it as out straight as this before and it was all to do with my new-found sacked voice. He didn't like that. Yes, the very first time I articulate out loud and clear what I really think, straight to his face, ever, and he lashes back with venom. Poisonous. It justified my previous long-held silences. Completely. So it was now to be tit-for-tat.

He continued, 'As soon as they have nothing left to sell they'll have to deal with the priests with red trousers, Cinders my dear. And let's see them survive then, with their degenerate junky lives.'

Tick tock tick tock. It was ten minutes to five o'clock and red mist drenched the insides of my normally well-jockeyed mind.

'If you can say that, then I can say this, Mister Purple.'

'You can call me Al now, Cinders, you've been sacked—remember? Five o'clock? Tick tock. Kaboom!'

I took a deep breath, looked him dead in the eyes.

'Alan, it's just like you and your like to say something like that. The middle-classes get very upset about bad language. Don't they? You're all the same. Most of the bad language that upsets you so has sexual connotations, like fuck or bastard or cunt. You know what I mean? If a middle-class person is shocked to the core of their very being by this sort of common-or-garden language, then they must be repressed. Sexually repressed if you ask me. It's a logical conclusion, Al.

'All middle-class people are sexually repressed, which means their parents must be too. And that they've passed it on to their offspring. Which means that they must have sexually abused their children. All middle-class people are paedophiles. It's logical and follows on conclusively. Paedophiles beget paedophiles. This paedophilia mixes in with their inherent greed and messes them up so much, that, although they have more than adequate professional salaries, they can never be as happy as the working classes. Not even close.

'Every action in a middle-class household is based on money and keeping it in the family, so much so, that the strain dehumanises their lives. The only way they can survive without killing themselves is to feel superior financially and morally to the working classes at whatever cost. They're only really happy when they're sexually abusing their own children or the children of the working classes, like in the 1950s up to the 1990s as priests or teachers or sports coaches in the community. Beyond that even and into the present tense. Their whole life is dedicated to this process. This is my own personal anecdotal evidence, Alan, like your own personal anecdotal Ballyfermot evidence.

'So Al, that's the middle classes for you in a nutshell. That's you. A greedy fucked-up paedophile. Excuse the Irish like.'

Yes, he was white-foaming at the mouth, truly, madly, deeply now, as I'd expected, so obviously I left the premises quite sharply with my governmental email, freshly snatched, in my hand. Maybe I laid it on a bit thick there, but fuck it. Cinderella's Left Testicle would play their final gig in the Pigeon Club that evening, I was determined. More so now. All I had to do was avoid the priests in red trousers and get to Markievicz Park for my rendezvous with Freddy. It would of course be quite dangerous, as I was now officially an intern, and was thus compelled to salute any priest in red trousers that passed me in the street. If you saluted their tri-colour flag-hat for long enough and with enough deference, they gave you food. But I'd just been sacked and wasn't that hungry yet. Maybe tomorrow. Anyway, I had that gig to play where Cinderella's Left Testicle were debuting a new song, and I needed to discuss the bones of it large with Freddy in the park.

Alan Purple went running to his locker for his baseball bat. He'd usually take this out at random times during the day and hit people that worked for him over the head with it, if he thought they weren't working hard enough. It was in one of the subsections of the new *Lazy Scumbag* legislation that authorized him to do so, and he took to it like a duck to water it has to be said. Then again, he'd always been a duck.

It was still technically two minutes to five o'clock in Alan's head, and if he was fast, agile and accurate enough, and got the right connect with the bat, he'd be able to leave my head bleeding for at least two days. Smack. Hospitals were now *verboten* to interns as well, as they'd proved themselves lazy scumbags by getting sacked in the first place, or so the logic went, ever onwards to some crazy conclusion I didn't really want to dwell upon, just the songs. Yeah, woman, just the songs.

Freddy and I had released three albums over the internet in the previous three years, and we were now working on the fourth, so there was a lot of headspace to be gripped onto and into in order to get the new song just right. Too much in fact. I had my gear already packed from earlier, so was out of my now former workplace and sprinting down the road in no time, leaving Alan Purple and his bloody baseball bat lagging well behind.

I reached the corner and looked into my bag to make sure the pyjamas were still inside. Smiling suns, they were. My brother, P.J. Tips, had made them for me. I was tempted to change into them right there on the spot and run past all the rich priests with red trousers lining the streets, flicking the V-signs, and definitely not saluting, definitely not. But no, I'd save that emotion for the new song at the Pigeoner later on that evening. Bottled emotion is always far better.

Shock! She's Wearing Pyjamas, was the title, my words, Freddy's music. But, as I turned the corner and gazed at the long stretch yet to walk, the job was obviously going to be a lot trickier than I'd initially calculated. Too many priests. Red trousers everywhere. Sally Bells, from the Pig warehouse across the road, was lovingly saluting one of these priests. Two of these priests. Three, four. She was about to collapse with exhaustion. Her expression said she'd been there hours. Still smiling though, fair play. That's Sally Bells alright. She might get a blueberry muffin out of it before long, thrown full-force at her face in the regulation manner by a red-trousered priest, to share with her family, for I'd heard that they were all interns now.

While I surveyed Sally's ossified smile, a priest came at me from behind and booted me hard up the back of the spine, which sent me flying with both arms downwards onto the gravel footpath, causing tiny fragments to embed in my palms and to bring forth blood and a certain amount of wincing. But I picked myself up and ran down Cromwellsfort Road towards the Walkinstown roundabout. If I was anything, I was fast, and I carried the new song in my head like a helium balloon, trying to recollect all the words. My own words, freshly sculpted from my life. I was nearly airborne.

On my way the priests stuck their legs out continually and tried to boot me hard up the back of the spine. In recent times, the priests of Ireland had developed quite a taste for kicking and punching, young women in particular. It was as if some strange valve released when the *Lazy Scumbag* legislation got passed by the government.

I glided past them all, though, each and every attacking priest, out in force on Cromwellsfort Road and Walkinstown Road, right up to Kylemore. Hundreds of interns saluting for food on the pavements, which was something I'd be doing in the next few days, if I didn't find a different path.

My new intern job was to begin on Monday in posh Blackrock, I repeated to myself like a mantra, to get used to it, a place I'd never been to physically. Not that path though. I was technically supposed to salute for food in the area in which I interned from Monday onwards. But the legislation stated that you couldn't pass a red-trousered priest without giving a quick salute or receiving a boot up the spine. So convoluted. I couldn't keep up. It was changing too fast, almost every day.

I made it down Kylemore eventually, without further spinal damage, and finally into Markievicz Park. I sprinted where I saw Freddy with his notebook open wide on his lap, scribbling into it distractedly. I sat down on the grass beside him, our usual euonymus scrub keeping us well hidden from any stray priests strolling.

'It's probably Cinderella's Left Testicle's last gig tonight, Freddy. I'm an intern in a Blackrock mansion from Monday. I'll be working every Friday from here on in. I won't get home until after twelve o'clock if I'm lucky, and I'll be on call for the rest of the night too. It's all shit Freddy. Everything is faeces.'

'I know, Cinders. I'm starting at the Nailing Planks factory tomorrow in leafy Terenure. It'll take me two hours to walk in to it in the mornings, what with my bad leg.'

'I thought only interns work there?'

'Up until yesterday, Cinders, that was true enough. A new subsection of the legislation passed by the government late last night has changed everything though. It means, in effect, that people with any lack of power over any of their limbs have been re-classified for hard labour as scumbags as well. The new austerity. That means me, Cinders.'

I threw my arms around him.

'It's just not fair. There has to be another way.'

'Don't worry, Cyn. I'm going to use the time it takes me to walk in each morning for writing more songs for The Testicle. It'll be grand. There's a voice recorder on my mobile. Very good quality. We'll have another album down pat in no time whatsoever. We'll probably have more subject material now for songs as well. Just think of the characters we'll soon meet. Infinite possibilities. The Nailing Planks factory in Terenure. Next album title?'

'Perhaps.'

'Not perhaps. Definitely, Cinders. Definitely.'

'How are you getting on with *Shock! She's Wearing Pyjamas*? Do you think there's enough words?'

'Of course there is, Freddy. Your melody is a thick stew. You can't distract from that with too many words. We just keep it simple and dish it out calmly, one spoonful at a time. Trust me on this one, Freddy. I've got good feelings. It makes me feel special.'

'So fucking special?'

'Yeah, you've got it,' I said.

'What about your brother's urine? Can we really use that tonight, Cinders? I'd like to, in fact you know I'd love to, but is it going too far?'

'Not for our last gig it's not, Freddy. You're not losing your balls, are you? We've been doing this for three years, surely they're golden by now? Clunk-clink. At this stage, our audience would drink three large mugs of my brother's urine, if we asked them to, with a pink cocktail umbrella sticking out the top, let alone the tiny splash that's in the new song. Did you ever know that we're their heroes? The wind beneath, anyway, you sing it only once or twice in the song, and Janey Macken Street, Freddy, what an effect to hit them with.'

I took my guitar out, Freddy studied his lyric sheet and off we went into Cinderella's Left Testicle's last official rehearsal.

We were surrounded on the skinhead grass by hundreds of scattered Jinny Joes; white dandelion clocks. A sharp wind blew diagonal for a few seconds, right through the fresh melody on our lips and fingertips. Each fuzzy-white Jinny Joe swaying in the breeze became the head of one of our fans in the Pigeon Club of a Friday evening, come to new life in the here and now of a Markievicz Park early summer. Swaying. Conkers Kavo, Finbarr Fist, Black Eyed Susan, Adam Finger, Patty Pigs, Janey Macken Street, Willie Wednesday, Rodney Harrington, Sharon Shampoo. Many Jinny Joes skanking together. In rude-health trance with our music. Skank. Skank. Skank. And when the wind finally blew all their Jinny-Joe minds one by one into a million snow-flakes of white downy seeds floating in the breeze, the new song prepared and seemed to strengthen us, somehow, for what was yet to come in the relentless Irish recession.

John D. Kelly

currently lives in County Fermanagh but was brought up in a working-class housing estate in Belfast. He was aged nine when 'the troubles' erupted in 1968. For many parents, education was one way for their children to get beyond the culture of sectarianism, discrimination and the insidious control of organized religion. John qualified as an architect in the mid-eighties, and has worked since then in many areas of the profession including social/public housing. He recently achieved an Honours Degree in Psychotherapy (a lifelong interest alongside poetry) and now practices in private practice and in 'low-cost' counselling centres in Ireland—north and south. He still practices, part-time, in architecture and continues to write poetry that's been award-winning and published in many literary magazines and anthologies. His debut collection *The Loss Of Yellowhammers* is to be published by Summer Palace Press in 2020.

Meandering

I'm driving downhill, going round the bend of a narrow country road. It's long and winding. Each bend winds in one direction only, but when they all join up, their sum seems snake-like, like the way lives often seem to be serpentine, like slow-flowing rivers are, or like the way I seem to go off on one, like now, before I catch myself on. It often seems as if people that are living such existences, just drift and meander as if in rudderless boats; a bit like it is for me and 'er it would seem. We're not really sailing in any purposeful direction or even on an even keel today, even on this fine and sunny morning; and she isn't speaking much either (apart from 'Digger!') and she's virtually useless as a reader of the map she has unfolded and spread out in front of her. She has no reading glasses with her and can thus only gaze through the windscreen, searching and scanning the ever-changing horizon that's continuously rolling towards us from the distance.

It is 17th March 2013, a Sunday. I think of St. Patrick who's supposed to have banished the snakes from this green land—even from this northern part—but I wonder if something of their fork-tongued aspect still lingers here as we go through the wee village of Harryville. We drive past the infamous 'Church of Our Lady'—site of many sectarian attacks since it opened in 1968, and the scene of bitter demonstrations in the 1990s. I'm aware that it's soon to be razed to the ground, but there are no JCBs here yet. We drive on, and pass the now fading, but obviously once colourfully painted red, white and blue surfaces of the concrete kerbstones of a mini-roundabout. Archaeologists now say that the marble stones of the Parthenon were originally painted in bright shades of blue, red, gold and green . . . *red, gold and green.*

I can't help but go off on one, again—on one of my own wee roundabouts as I imagine Boy George, wearing a weirdly-tall bowler hat, singing 'Karma

Chameleon' and wearing a dress with a sash and doing his queer dance alongside her uncle Billy, at the head of an Orange March, around those famous columns in Athens.

I must be as mad as Carroll's Hatter, or like the hares I'm hoping to see chasing one another and 'boxing' in the fields that skirt Slemish. I recall seeing my first one of those magical creatures with my father when I was last there as a ten-year-old boy.

I slow down, wind down the passenger window, and lean over her to ask a well-dressed, but seemingly dour-looking man (about my age) for directions to the strangely shaped volcanic rock that is Slemish. We remember from geography lessons in our respective colleges in Belfast that the mountain we seek formed 60 million years ago as the 'plug' of an extinct volcano. Paleontologists reckon that dinosaurs became extinct on Earth approximately 6 million years prior to its formation; but I'm aware that there are some people who live in these parts who don't hold with such scientific certainties. She often distances herself from that side of her family by calling them 'the flat earth brigade'—those who live in a land where time stands still. Jokingly, but half-seriously too, she says that a particular species of dinosaur still roams the plains here.

The man that we try to talk to has a bovine-looking, ruddy-red face. He's dressed in his Sunday best and really does seem to be from some other age. He has a cold, blank expression in his eyes; and, before I catch myself on again, I think I was actually measuring the distance between them in my mind! I've already judged and labelled him as a staunch Loyalist and a bigot. I've no doubt, in my sick head, that he does know which road we should take when he shakes what I see as his big Planter's head, smirks, shrugs his shoulders and stays shtum. He seems more interested in noting the green of our Landrover, than in sharing his local knowledge. I even have it in my shamefully prejudiced head that he knows that the 'Tonga' of 'Landrover Tonga Green' comes from the Polynesian word *fakatonga* which means southwards, and that he can actually smell my Fenian blood and sense that I have at least some roots or connection to the southern Free State. We leave him standing there and drive on and, in spite of what I self-righteously judge to be *his* 'sectarian silence', that iconic mountain's unmistakable, bluish outline soon appears on the horizon.

'The Long and Winding Road', from 1969, is playing on the radio, but it's hard to hear it above the tractor-like rhythm in the heart of our old, rusty, beat-up Defender, whose doors don't close properly anymore. I suddenly feel like a sick, green cliché. I don't know where this is all leading to, or why my head is now off remembering the door of our house in Fernagh Estate in North Belfast. Our front door was painted with a green cross (in oil-based gloss) one 11th night, in the same year that the Beatles track we're listening to now was released. I was only ten then. I think now of Kristallnacht and the words of Mary McAleese, in 2005, that got her into a bit of 'bother', as Patrick Kavanagh might have put it.

I think, too, of Proust's *À La Recherche Du Temps Perdu*, and wonder what has triggered me, this time, to bring me back there; and then I'm off with that other Marcel—not the mime artist Marceau, but . . . Duchamp, the guy who took the piss with a urinal and called it Art; and then I'm back with her. She's still here, beside me, and I hear her from the passenger seat:

'Digger!', as we drive on.

I really, really don't know where this is all leading me to, as I drive on into the interior of this ancient landscape through each chicane. I love the word chicane and am aware that it derives from the French word *chicaner*, which means 'to create difficulties', 'to pointlessly argue' or 'to quibble'. I have always loved the etymology of words. I remember that I looked up the word 'meander' once and found that it derives from the Greek river *Maiandros*, which has a particularly winding course on the tail-end of its slow-flowing journey to the Aegean Sea. In its Latin origin, the noun 'meander' means a 'confusion or intricacy'. I'm certainly nothing if not extremely confused by the flow in me on this strange morning. It's as if I'm embarking on Homer's Greek *Odyssey* or at least on a local journey that now feels epic. I turn to look at the side of her beautiful face and think of Van Morrison, and then our favourite song (even though her eyes are green); but my girl is still only 'picture – no sound' apart from . . . 'Digger!'

Our old neighbour, Mr. Fitzsimons, used to say that of his wife Audrey: 'picture—no sound' when they would have the odd quibble or squabble, and he'd sheepishly come to the back door of our house for some respite or refuge and to confide in my father who would, more often than not, offer him a wee Bush in our kitchen—a glass of Bushmills whiskey that is—and generally not a 'wee' one. Perhaps Mr. Fitzsimmons only used that line to get some sympathy and the always generously filled glass; or perhaps it was my dad who used those occasions as excuses to justify having one himself? I'm not too sure, but I think it was more the latter!

As I ponder these memories, my father is now 'into his eighty-seventh year' as he would put it. My mother will be eighty-nine if she makes it to her next birthday in December.

I now have the perspective and wisdom of history and parenthood to help me appreciate the stress he was living under (they both were living under) and why my mother always gave him a by-ball for any of his minor misdemeanours when 'in his cups'. Those were difficult and dangerous times in which to rear a family.

I was only ten when the Fitzsimons's lived in the house adjoining ours. They too were Catholics, and I remember they also had a green cross painted on their front door that 11th of July night in 1969, as did all the Catholic families living in our predominantly Protestant housing estate at that time.

What is it about Man that he needs to mark and label people and land with symbols and flags, or attempt to control them with an 'in-your-face' foot-tramping of territory; or, as it was in this case, by 'we know where you live' intimidation, and the almost biblical daubing of doors?

Thankfully, I'm abruptly snapped out of the tailspin of these dark memories by:

'Digger! That's six—three to me!' And I'm so glad to at last sense a softening in her tone and see her flash those killer pearly whites at me.

The game we've been playing is 'The Digger Game'—one point for each JCB (or other make of earth-scooping plant) spotted on our journey. My dad invented this game, many years ago, to keep me, my brother and two sisters entertained during long journeys across the border to the sanctuary of the West of Ireland, and when 'I Spy' became tedious and overly-complicated. We still play it quite often, even without our own sons, and we've found it can serve as an ice-breaker when things get a bit stuck between us.

'Ok, you win!'

I concede it, as we arrive in the car park at the foot of our destination.

'Hard for me to win, mind you, when I'm the one who's driving and concentrating on the sharp bends.'

'Tough!'

She smiles, as she jumps out and hares off:

'First one to the summit gets another prize!'

Off she goes, knowing I have still to put on my hiking boots and lock all the doors to the Defender individually, as the central locking no longer works. By the time I get on my way she's already well ahead. I take a deep breath and give chase.

*

Back in Harryville, a fifty-five-year-old man with the mental age of a boy of about ten is returning home from mass. His ninety-year-old mother, who would normally take him, is ill and in bed with her rosary beads. He can't wait to get back to playing with his collection of toy Landrover Defenders. He has every model, going right back to the first one launched in 1948; but firstly he goes into her with a cup of tea and some toast.

'Good boy!' she says, 'Now tell me . . . did you do as I said and not talk to any strangers on the way?'

'No, Mammy, I didn't say a word to nobody, not even to the two strangers in the Tonga Green, long wheelbase, 110 2.4 TD County Station Wagon, 5d. with the snorkel and the full rack and hi-beam spots. They asked me for directions to Slemish, Mammy, but I didn't say a word; just like you said Mammy.'

'Good boy, John-Patrick, good boy.'

*

With a few metres to spare, I catch up and overtake her on the steepest part of the slope and make it to the summit first. When she arrives she collapses into my arms. We are both panting and exhausted. Our eyes meet.

'Ok', I grin, 'it's one—all, and . . . sorry . . . I was wrong, again. Can we call it quits?'

We open up and melt together as we shape-shift into another form, like two prize boxers embracing and merging their complementary colours after a long and bloody bout.

Mary Lennon

comes from working-class Walkinstown—new 50s suburb, swallowing green fields, indifferent to its bordering historic villages, Crumlin & Tallaght.

Class was fine distinctions: fathers' jobs, clean & dirty—suits/overalls; similarly, mothers' domains—messy/well-kept houses—families 2/3 kids—clean; 4 plus—messy, like ours.

Class was stories, songs, passed on by my Mayo mother, Dublin father, and his single sister who gifted me with books birthdays & Christmas—*Little Women, Chalet School*—manna from heaven, albeit confirming that books were about other lives, never ours.

Class was nuns who pushed the *promising*, with parents who *sacrificed*, to get us to Leaving Cert. English poems, essays my favourites; I also scribbled in diaries, which I showed to nobody. *A Writer—You kidding?*

But stories drove me, beginning with Irish women in England, published by Virago, later stories inside my head, which I continually write & sometimes publish.

Taken by a Gangsta

Ali arrived, late again, completely wired, 'Clare told me the whole thing!'

Jack shoved the beer towards her, 'Yeh?'

She took a slug, 'Happened twenty-two years ago, was all over the papers, on TV. Her Dad went out to back a few horses, buy fags—the usual Saturday—never came back.'

'Never?'

'Uh-huh. Police searched everywhere, tracker dogs dragged the river, neighbours searched, her Mam went on TV, *Please, please, come home if you're out there* ... you know the kinda thing.'

'And nothing?'

'Zilch. It got hard at school, *Your Da was taken by a gangsta?*—that kinda crack. Eventually, police, newspapers gave up, just her mother putting up posters for years, until hope was killing them.'

'It explains Clare being ... weird.'

Clare was deep weird.

'Yeh. They moved to Dublin, started over.'

Ali finally noticed his empty.

'Another pint?'

'Yes please.'

She ordered, then jumped straight back into it. 'Anyways ... one afternoon Clare leaves work early, someone cancelled, pure fluke, she's on the Piccadilly Line, watching this boy reading *Harry Potter*, reminds her of her nephew. At Arsenal, a man standing up, moves, takes the boy's hand to leave; she glances up and there—he—feckin—is!'

'Who?'

'The father!'

'Jesus.'

'Older, bit grey ... but she'd no doubt. Got off, followed them all the way until they arrived at their house. They're about to go inside, and out it came, one single word, *DAD?* Loud.'

'And?'

'He froze, slowly turned, said, Madeline? That's her look-alike sister.'

'*Clare*, she said. Nobody moved, three statues, standing staring.'

'Did he..?'

'She walked away.'

'Oh. Eye for an eye?'

'No. She saw a brick in the garden, decided to smash his head in, watch the blood gushing down the path.'

'Ah, c'mon?'

'Dead serious, she was in a rage zone, could've done it, but the boy was watching her ... like he... kinda knew. Said she couldn't do it to him.'

Jack sat, let it sink in.

*

Dave Lordan

born to Irish parents in Derby in 1975, returned to Ireland in '77. After hod carrying in the UK, his father worked as a dynamiter in the Baryte mine at Dunmore, West Cork, until 1981, then unemployed or casually employed until the mid-90s. His mother worked numerous menial jobs, now as a home-help. His two brothers are bricklayers. Dave started work as a night baker at fourteen in Houlihans bakery in 1990, and has been in continuous employment since, apart from study breaks, in everything from construction to university lecturing. In 1992, aged sixteen, he became the first person on his housing estate to finish school; received a degree in literature at nineteen. Became involved in socialist activism at age fifteen, going at it since.

Privilege

Years later, when I think of him, what rises up is the famous lasagne, which he himself cooked, and which was such a surprise to the rest of us.

No-one would have credited that a bedsit chronic like Jim could even conceive of lasagne, never mind get around to cooking it.

But Jim had invited us all around to his place that Friday night for a 'dinner party', and it turned out that, despite all our sniggering at the absurdity of the idea, he had meant it.

I don't remember what the lasagne tasted like, just the look of it, the part-browned top layer of cheese, appetising and aromatic—real lasagne. I remember Jim drunkenly pulling it out of the oven and holding it up to show off before multiple witnesses that it truly existed. I remember him explaining that he had got the brown effect by putting it under the grill for five minutes after the bake, a trick of the trade he had learned from his cousin, a chef in London, and which could also be used to round off Spanish omelettes and the like.

We were all already twisted on buckfast and hot-knives, of course. We wolfed down the lasagne, and the homemade garlic bread.

I reckon that was Jim's last ever party. His everlasting party. We all went back home to recover Sunday morning, or afternoon at the latest, but it lasted Jim the rest of his life.

St Vincent De Paul took over shortly after. They gave him shoes and clothes and toothpaste and food—all things which were more or less completely useless to him. But I think they paid his rent too, or at least shielded him from eviction. I knew Ted, his landlord, well—it's a small town —Ted was a real schemer and he couldn't wait to get rid of Jim and get new regular tenants in.

Sometimes me or one of the lads would drop up with a flagon or two and a packet of tobacco as a gift for Jim, out of our old fondness and our wish to not see him suffer too badly.

The DT's is a hard road, trampled by merciless elephants that do not exist, but who can crush the last wheeze out of you nonetheless.

Jim's last eyes were small and round and fearful and moist and full of poison. They looked at you like any pestilence might look at you. They seemed to draw the life out of everything they took in. You felt a little paler every time.

His last hands were calloused and cracked, as if, all his life, he had been handling corrosives. It was hard to avoid shaking hands with him—he was such an in-your-face, needy kind of drunk—but I did avoid it, even at the risk of causing offence. I simply held my hands behind my back any time he came near me. I didn't want to catch anything. Everything about Jim was consumed by disease. He himself was a consuming disease. Things became sick by belonging to or associating with him. He had a sick settee, a sick radio, sick T-shirts and shoes, a sick toothbrush for his glistening sick teeth, a sick old guitar with one string, a sick pair of cheap sunglasses he wore around the bedsit, as if the sun of July were always above him. He had a sick past full of sick memories. And sick friends like me. His sick listeners.

During these last visits Jim often spoke to us of a son he'd had many years ago, with an ex-girlfriend with whom he had broken up before the child had been born. We had never before heard of the child, nor the girlfriend. He said he was hoping to make contact again with the child, now seventeen years of age. The son was, according to Jim, some kind of international martial arts prodigy. The son was playing for Ireland, Jim said, covered in glory and touring the world. Jim was waiting for the son to turn eighteen, when he would be able to legally make contact. This fantasy animated Jim greatly whenever he spoke of it, but weeks could go by when he wouldn't make mention.

Another last thing he told me was that he had stopped shitting. I said that was because he had stopped eating. He said life was much less complicated when you neither ate nor shat.

The last thing he spoke of was time. He said that he had learned to move around inside time. He said he could travel up and down his own life like it was a bridge. A bridge connecting nothing to nowhere, he said. There's a black hole at either end of us, he said.

Sometimes he went back to his deep childhood, just to watch himself sleeping as a little boy. This was very calming, he said. The blankets undulated noiselessly, he said, like a secret sea. He said that deaf sailors had the most beautiful lives. He never snored when he was little. He often went to his own funeral too. There was a bigger crowd at it than he would have expected, given all the people he had pissed off over the years and all the snobs there were in our town. He was troubled by reports of another local drunk who had recently died by smoke inhalation during a house fire—only the priest, another notorious sozzler, had gone to that funeral. The visions—or whatever you want to call them—settled him down.

I dreamt last night that I killed him, that Ted the landlord had given me four grand to beat him to death with a hammer. I can clearly see his face, gripped with shock and agony after the first blow. I see his hand on his broken head and the thick gunk streaming out between his fingers.

Then I strike him again, and again, until the job's done.

For some time after I woke up from this dream I believed it had really happened and I felt oppressed by my guilt. Never before had a dream made such perfect sense.

Anne Mac Darby-Beck

was born into a working-class family in rural County Laois. When she left school she worked in a factory until being made redundant. She moved to Kilkenny, married a tradesman and had a child. After working in various jobs over the years she now works for the local authority. She wrote extensively as a child, but fell away from the practice in her late teens. She joined a women's study group in a local village, which morphed into a writers' group. With the encouragement of the group she began to write again. She writes poems and short stories in her free time outside of work and home. Her poems and stories have been published in various anthologies and magazines such as *Cyphers, Poetry Ireland Review, Crannog, Skylight 47, 1916–2016 Anthology of Reactions, A New Ulster*, etc. She won a first place in Syllables Poetry Competition.

Sick Day

She stood before the blind and offered up a silent prayer. *Please Lord*, she thought, *please don't send any dickheads my way today*. However, the moment she raised the blind and saw the man wearing a scowl outside, she knew the Lord Almighty would not answer her prayers today. She unlocked the outer door, turned quickly to enter the inner door code, and escaped to the safety of the office. The man walked in and banged the ticket down on the counter.

'Why did I get this?' he asked.

She looked at the ticket. It said 'Parking in a disc parking area without displaying a disc.' The question seemed to answer itself, if the man could read, but she knew the score here.

'Good morning,' she said, 'this ticket has only just been issued so won't be on my system yet, but it seems to say ...'

Of course this wasn't what he was looking for. He knew why he had gotten the ticket. He was just cheesed off and was looking for a punching bag.

'I was only five fucking minutes,' he said, his voice rising, 'you're allowed the first fifteen minutes free. Those fucking wardens are wankers. How much commission will that bastard get for this?'

She tried to slow her breathing and remain calm.

'The wardens are not on commission, Sir, and he would have logged your car and given you ...'

Sometimes, she thought, they could just put an automated message on the counter in her place because that was all she was. She repeated the same obvious things, over and over, to people who took a chance and just would not take responsibility when they got caught.

'I don't give a fuck; I was only there five fucking minutes. You bastards in the Council have business ruined and everyone driven out of the town. I want to talk to someone higher up.'

Good luck with that, she thought. Managers do not lead the troops;

they hide back in the ranks. She offered him an appeal form. He told her he was a busy man and didn't have time to appeal a 'fucking fine' the 'bastard' warden should never have given him. He walked out still shouting, but did take the form with him.

The office fell silent. She sighed and turned back to her desk. Another great start to the week, and it was a week she would be working alone. She was no sooner sitting down when the door opened again. She began to rise.

'Oh, don't trouble yourself to get up,' the man said, sarcastically, 'I just want to know where the police station is.'

She felt her jaw clench.

'Sorry, Sir, the what?'

He tutted in annoyance.

'I have to pay a speeding fine,' he said.

'Oh, you mean the *Garda* station,' she said innocently. 'I have a map here with the *Garda* station marked, Sir, no problem at all.'

Her next customer was an American tourist looking for a 'rest room'. The Irish language may be dying, she thought, but the English language is doing no better. When he was gone, she tried to get some work done but heard the door open again. However, this time, it was Tommy Devlin, a council tenant. They had a bit of craic while she was receipting his rent.

Time came for a cup of tea, if she could find a peaceful minute to have one. The office was usually manned by three staff, but because everyone was on holiday, this week she was alone. You could complain, but they had subtle ways of making you pay. The manager had said to her 'Oh, call on me if you're busy.' But if you tried doing that, you got a cold shoulder for the rest of the day. She munched on her sandwich and sipped her tea.

She was bending down behind her screen, putting her lunch box in her bag, when the door opened.

'Hello, hello, is anyone here?' said a well-to-do voice.

She stood up.

'Oh, I thought the office was unattended,' the woman said, sounding slightly disappointed.

She was about to comment, but thought better of it.

'I want a resident's parking permit,' the woman said, 'for my holiday home. I don't live there all the time but want one for when I'm back.'

She did not have the form filled in, and when her documents were checked, half were missing.

'We'll need the insurance certificate and a utility bill,' she told the woman.

She could see the woman's temper rising; she could write the script on this.

'Utility bill? What on earth is a utility bill? I don't live here; I have no idea what you're talking about.'

She tried showing her the form where it was written exactly what was needed to get a resident's parking permit. The woman was not having any of it.

'This is nonsense', she spat irritably, grabbed the documents and left.

Half an hour later, she was back. She produced the insurance certificate, but no utility bill.

'There's a document with my PPS number. That should be sufficient for you.'

She tried pointing out the rules attached to getting a permit, and why they were in place. The woman rudely demanded she just issue the permit. Realising she was getting nowhere, she decided to ring the manager upstairs. But while she was trying to talk to her manager, the woman shouted over her.

'Who are you talking to? Give me back my documents. I will speak to this person.'

She grabbed the documents and walked out, muttering 'You're useless' as her parting shot.

She sat back down. There has to be easier ways to make a living, she thought. The door opened and the manager walked in with the woman in tow. They were chatting amicably. How different her tone was. The manager came into the office but did not meet her eye—always a bad sign.

'We'll take this document with the PPS number instead of a utility bill,' the manager said.

She felt her face redden, her stomach lurch.

'It's not a utility bill,' she said quietly.

The manager folded her arms.

'It has her PPS number on it.'

So what, she thought. She turned to the counter. The woman was standing on the other side, smirking. The manager turned to go. The woman, laying it on thick, said 'Thank *you* soooo much'.

She receipted the money and wrote out the permit. The woman snatched it and left.

She sat down at her desk and felt like crying. She decided not to ring the manager until she had calmed down a little. She ran all the usual sobering reminders through her head: they were all dickheads; being on the bottom rung of the ladder, or a 'lower grade' as the media liked to call it, meant they could treat you like shit; no manager was ever going to have your back when you're trying to enforce rules they made. She picked up the phone.

'Are we taking documents with a PPS number on it now, in place of a utility bill?' she asked.

There was a pause.

'I need to know if the rules have changed.'

There was an irritated sigh.

'Well, no, but we have to use our common sense. In a case like this ...'

'That woman treated me like shit,' she said.

The manager tutted.

'Well, she was nice to me...'

She was at the roundabout and on her road home before she stopped, banging the steering wheel, and shouted, *bitch, bitch, bitch*. She screeched up the drive and rushed into the house, dumping her bags and hastily pulling on her cycling gear. She opened the shed door, pulled out her bike and went cycling back the road she had just driven. The pedals turned and she fell into rhythm, her legs pumping them round and round. She cut through the wind, head down, pushing her legs as hard as she could. By the time she reached halfway along her route, she felt calmer. It was the manager she hated most. The public treat you like a dogsbody. But the manager bent the rules when it suited and then hung you out to dry. They left you wide open, to be sneered at by a woman who believed the rules should not apply to her, because she was rich enough to afford a holiday home. The words of her favourite writer came to her: *privilege means private law*. It would serve the manager right if she was out sick tomorrow. Then she would have to do the counter on her own and take all the flak from the public. As she cycled, the thought strengthened in her mind. She hated skiving off, but when you get treated like that, well .... fuck it. By the time she cycled back up the drive, it was decided. Tomorrow she would take a sick day.

The End

Tomás Mac Síomóin

Born in 1938 of Dublin working-class, and Roscommon hill farmer stock, active IRA militants in the Tan War, 1918-21. A Cornell University doctoral graduate and biology researcher/lecturer in the USA and Ireland. IRA membership was an early influence. His translation into Irish of *The Communist Manifesto* was published in 1986 by the CPI, of which he was a member. His involvement with Irish stemmed from extended periods in the Gaeltacht. He edited the Irish-language publications *Comhar* and *Anois*. Has published poems, short stories and novels in Irish (some translated into English were published by Nuascéalta). Also non-fiction, such as the landmark *The Broken Harp* and its companion volume, *Gael becomes Irish*, examining in depth the enduring effects of colonialism on the Irish psyche and on the fortunes of the Irish language. He has written in, and translated from, Spanish. A resident of Catalonia for over twenty years.

Ballyfermot Enigma!

Urban Ballyfermot didn't exist a century ago.

But faced with a pressing need to alleviate overcrowding in the Central Dublin City area, and eliminate tenements that housed much of Dublin's working class, the farms of rural Ballyfermot, beyond Inchicore to the west of Dublin city, were acquired by the urban authorities in the 1930s. They were developed into suburban housing estates needed also to ease the post-war housing shortage. The first estate was built in the late 1940s at Ballyfermot Lower. During the 1970s Ballyfermot suffered from unemployment and a lack of facilities and opportunities for its residents. However, contemporary Ballyfermot possesses a range of educational and recreational facilities.

Nevertheless, Ballyfermot, to borrow from the lexicon of the renowned English journalist, Owen Jones, author of *Chavs: The Demonisation of the Working Class*, was regarded by non-residents as the Irish capital of Chav. In this groundbreaking work, Jones charts how the British working class, 'chavs', went from being 'the salt of the earth' to being 'the scum of the earth'. This caricature, based on media obsession with the evils of an indigent white working class, is used by governments to avoid social and economic problems and to justify inequality.

Thus, we find the following internet description of Ballyfermot: 'This charming suburb, categorised as one of 'Dublin's NO-GO areas, offers one of the highest chances of getting assaulted in Dublin. Outsiders are not looked at very kindly, which has helped maintain the indigenous demographics of the area—a great preservation of culture tactic indeed!' This cryptic reference to Ballyfermot by a Mr. Prateek Sharma, reflects a commonly held predjudice, cultivated by Dublin's popular media—faithfully mirroring their British templates as Irish media are wont to do—that this working-class area consists almost solely of criminal elements. Not all denizens of Ballyfermot are squeaky clean and virtuous—crime statistics for the area do not support such a claim—but the majority of 'Bally-er' inhabitants, in my experience, are decent, companionable, hard-working citizens.

Friends of mine, Mícheál, Antóin and myself, all Irish speakers, were approached by Ballyfermot acquaintances in 1995, with a request to hold Irish classes on Sunday mornings for interested working people and pensioners from their area, all English speakers who were keen to learn the Irish language. There were suitable premises available for this purpose—namely, the comfortable licensed premises of the Liffey Gaels GAA Club, situated on the Inchicore-Ballyfermot border. If the class commenced at 11.00 a.m., it was suggested, and ended at 12.30 p.m., its termination would coincide with the opening of the club bar, a happy event that would facilitate continuation of said class, but in a more informal and relaxed social atmosphere.

Thanks to this ubiquitous Covid-19 plague and our rigid lockdown (I live now in Catalonia), my diary of those years is not to hand and I am at the mercy of a sometimes faulty memory. Summers excluded, I trudged out every Sunday morning from central Dublin, where I then lived, alongside the River Liffey, passing Kingsbridge Railway Station and onwards to the Liffey Gaels' clubhouse, where the other teachers and a group of eager learners awaited us. Most of these learners had acquired almost no Irish from their earlier primary schooling. Furthermore, from the point of view of the 'teachers' (though the teacher-pupil relation was replaced by a friend-friend one) there were no suitable texts adequate to our purpose (for reasons explained below). So we ad-libbed to a large extent. In time, with the expansion of numbers attending classes, some of the 'pupils' became 'teachers'.

A thoroughly useful, and enjoyable, feature of the 'school year' for both students and teachers, paid for by the class itself, was the annual stay in the Gaeltacht. Thus it was that we visited and stayed, in hostels or lodging with local people, in the Gleann Cholmcille Gaeltacht in SW Donegal, Scoil Uí Chadhain in the Ceathrú Rua (West Galway) Gaeltacht and in the Rath Cairn-Conamara Gaeltacht in nearby Meath. Thus, the students experienced the salient features of two major Irish dialects along with Gaeltacht social life, a veritable *terra incognita* for many of them, and, of course, the tastes and effects of sundry local brews.

Such was the enthusiasm of our 'students' for Irish, and the bonding that the classes engendered, that they decided to attempt to 'proselytize' in their area. Thus they carried out detailed surveys of the demand for Irish classes among adults in Ballyfermot and of the willingness of local shopkeepers to display Irish-language labelling of their for-sale produce. The response to this was highly positive, even enthusiastic, and was integrated into an Action Plan to strengthen the position of the Irish language in

Ballyfermot and to be enacted by the group. This Plan was forwarded to the then Bord na Gaeilge, with a request for funding to enable its execution. To my knowledge, we never received a formal response from An Bord. All the money available for such projects went to *Tiobrad Arann ag Caint*, an initiative to promote the speaking of Irish in Tipperary. For the second year running...

It was relayed to me that an officer of Bord na Gaeilge was heard to comment: what business have they (Ballyfermot people) with reviving Irish? Insinuating that Ireland's notional first language cannot be a valid concern of working-class citizens? I was to discover, as we shall see, that this attitude was by no means exceptional in the broad Irish language movement.

Another possibility is that the Bord had become acquainted with the Left political leanings of some of the teachers. These would not have been welcomed by Bord na Gaeilge and by highly influential members of the broad Irish language movement. In Ireland, one's ideological leanings, no matter how carefully guarded, become the common knowledge of one's employers and others. How could it have been otherwise, in my case, with a Special Branch car almost permanently parked just up the road from *New Books*, a left-wing bookshop in East Eccles Street, Dublin, that I frequently visited, that also happened to be the Communist Party of Ireland headquarters. There were various straws in the wind. Thus, the ubiquitous radio and print journalist, and fount of hot political gossip, Proinsias Mac Aonghusa, with whom I drove from Berlin to Halle (near Leipzig) in the then DDR, to deliver a lecture, would have been very well aware of my political adherence. He was in almost permanent close contact with leading members, of all political shades, of the Irish language movement. By no means a secretive individual, he often took an impish delight in letting cats out of bags....

Various other straws suggested that news of my politics had been leaked! On a social call to my house one evening in Raheny, Dublin, Conor Cruise O'Brien greeted me jocosely as 'old Party comrade'. Coincidence? At about the same time, at the formal launch of Teilifís na Gaeilge, forerunner of the present TG4, in Baile na hAbhann on the 31st of October 1996, a future President of Ireland, Mícheál D. Ó hUiginn TD, confided to me his dissatisfaction with the Labour Party. 'I should have become instead a member of the Communist Party of Ireland,' he said.

In other words, I suggest that the merest hint of leftist involvement in the modest Ballyfermot language movement may have triggered a negative response to our request for funding to develop Irish in the area. A rural initiative, *Tiobrad Arann ag Caint*, had already received a previous grant from Bord na Gaeilge, but now they were granted another. Financial assistance for the Ballyfermot project was refused.

Our experience with the Liffey Gaels classes, made me reflect on the efficiency of our teaching program. To expect speakers of a relatively non-inflected language (English) to adapt easily to the totally unfamiliar norms of a highly inflected one (that is riddled with exceptions to its rules), namely, standard/literary Irish, is unrealistic and counterproductive. The results of Irish-language tuition in most (non-Gaelscoil) secondary schools confirm this. An inordinate amount of time is spent memorising the cases of five categories of noun, and the declensions of regular and irregular verbs, and then trying to infiltrate all this complexity into the neophyte's ordinary conversational Irish. This unspeakably tedious practice is such a total waste of time that it leaves very many learners with an understandable hatred for the language. Native Gaeltacht residents speak a much more simply structured Irish. If learners were exposed to this form of the language, their speed of acquisition of colloquial Irish would be much more rapid...

For example, let's compare some 'learned Irish' forms with those described to me by an average middle-aged Connacht Gaeltacht informant in 1965. Nouns of the former often had three forms in both singular and plural categories according to the then Official Standard Irish. But the Gaeltacht form had only two: the singular and plural forms. Thus (Standard forms on the left, Connacht Gaeltacht forms to the right, in the table below):

An Bhean (Nominative Singular)	The Woman	An Bhean
Mála na Mná (Genitive Singular)	The Woman's bag	mála an bhean
Ar an Mnaoi (Dative Singular)	On the woman	ar an mbean ('b' silent)
Na Máthracha (Nominative Plural)	The Women	Na Máthracha
Na Máthar (Genitive Plural)	Of the Women	Na Máthracha
Ar na Mátharaibh/ Máthrachaibh (Dative Plural)	On the women	Ar Na Máthracha

My Gaeltacht informant let me know that nouns had only two forms in the speech of his native Gaeltacht island, singular (Bean) and plural (Mná). Savants attribute this simplification of Irish to corruption of their ideal classical grammar as reflected, for example, in Seathrún Céitinn's (Geoffrey Keating's) 17th century masterpiece, Foras Feasa ar Éirinn. But, would they describe the English of contemporary 20th century masters of prose in that language such as Kurt Vonnegut, J.G. Ballard or Liam O'Flaherty, for example, as being simply the results of the degeneration of the language of Beowulf, Chaucer and Shakespeare?

I put this conundrum before a leading Irish scholar and academic, a professor of Celtic studies and a present emeritus professor of the Dublin Institute of Advanced Studies, then a Professor of Irish at Trinity College Dublin. His response was simple and direct: 'students must be made to memorise all the grammar of the Official Standard (An Caighdeán). Only in that way can they really master the language.' But to what language was he

115

referring? Did he equate 'the language' with 'Official Standard Irish', with all of its archaisms, all but unknown in the living Gaeltacht? The response to the approach advocated by him is reflected in the results of many surveys of secondary school students that indicate that Irish is the most hated subject of their Leaving Cert. curricula...

To have students memorize the rules of a long-dead Irish makes absolutely no sense, unless the aim of such tuition is cultivation of the ability to access earlier literature. But if the aim of Irish-language tuition was acquisition of the ability to communicate with Gaeltacht residents, then the Irish taught should, logically, correspond to the language spoken day to day by Gaeltacht residents. Such Irish, is immeasurably less complex than the official standard language as taught to, for example, secondary students.

Why this vested interest in complexity? If one truly believed that the creation of a Gaelic-speaking mandarin class, to administer the affairs of the new quasi-independent Irish state was the only viable strategy to ensure the survival of Irish Gaelic culture, then the barrier of a complex mandarin language, with an impossible (for most learners) grammar, would be an impenetrable barrier to most non-speakers of Irish seeking a place within the ruling circle.

When this idea first occurred to me, I little realised how close I may have been to the mark.

Bhunaigh Gael Linn nuachtán seachtainiúil, *Anois*, sa mbliain 1984. B'in an chéad nuachtán lán-daite tablóideach i nGaeilge. Newspread Ltd, dáilitheoir tábhachtach mór-dhíola a scaip an nuachtán nua seo ar fud na tíre go dtí gur tháinig críoch leis i 1996. Chaitheas dhá bhliain, 1985–86, sílim (níl teacht ar mo dhialann don tréimhse úd) ag obair mar thuairisceoir agus, ar ball, mar Eagarthóir *Anois*. Ba é Dónal Ildánach Ó Móráin Stiúrthóir Bainistíochta an nuachtáin seo. Thug iliomad córáití leis an Móránach an tráth úd léargas neamhchoitianta dom ar mhachnamh is ar chur chuige an duine ba mhó tábhacht i saol na Gaeilge an tráth úd. Is ar mhachnamh a chomhleacaithe a mba 'dhaoine le seasamh'—téarma sár-mholtach i bhfoclóir Dhónail—chuile dhuine acu.

Scaoil cuid de na córáití seo rún saoil Uí Mhóráin le gaoth, chuile sheans.

Duine sár-chliste, sár-chasta, sár-chruthaíoch is sár-chumasach ab ea Dónal Ó Móráin. Fear a raibh creideamh daingean aige sna prionsabail a raibh sé geallta dóibh. Dar leis, níor chiallaigh Athbheochan na Gaeilge go dtiontódh an náisiún uilig ar an nGaeilge. Chiallaigh sé go mbeadh an Ghaeilge (nó Gaoluinn) slán dá mbeadh sí ina meán cumarsáide ag aicme mhaorlathach a rialódh an tír, cineál *herrenvolk*, mar a déarfá. Mar a dúirt sé liomsa babhta amháin, agus líon na scéalta in Anois a raibh baint acu le Tuaisceart Éireann agus le 'daoine gan tábhacht' (a shainmhíniú ar oibritheoirí) á cháineadh aige, ní foláir dúinn freastal feasta ar dhaoine le seasamh, óir is iadsan amháin a shealbhóidh agus a chinnteoidh buaine na Gaeilge.

Chreid sé ariamh sa ngá le *herrenvolk* Gaelach le haidhmeanna na hAthbheochana a bhaint amach. Ba dhlúthchuid riachtanach dá 'phacáiste' idé-eolaíochta luachanna coimeádacha sóch-eacnamaíocha Fhine Gael, an páirtí lenar thacaigh an Móránach ariamh. Is go láidir! *'Nach Léinte Gorma sinn ar fad*—a bhéiceadh sé amach scaití agus fonn ceiliúrtha air. Eagraíocht faisisteach Éireannach, bunaithe i 1932, í múnlaithe ag a mhacasamhail ar an Mór-Roinn, i dtriochaidí na haoise seo caite, ba iad na Léinte Gorma. Níor thimpist, dá réir sin, a spéis seisean sa iSóisialachas Náisiúnta. Ná a chnuasach de ghriangrafanna de Hitler agus de cheannairí faisisteacha eile de chuid na Gearmáine, na hIodáile, na Spáinne...

Bhain spéis Uí Mhóráin sa Chomhchaidreamh, cumann de Ghaeilgeoirí Tríú Leibhéil, leis an bhfonn a bhíodh air taisce saineolais agus ard-éirimiúlacht a chruthú a ghlacfadh le cúramaí ceannasaíochta agus bainistíochta Éire Ghaelach seo a shamhlaíochta. Nuair a scoir an eagraíocht seo sna 1990aí bhí baint aige le hiarrachtaí éagsúla leis an dé a chur ar ais sa chorp.

D'fhéach Dónal freisin lena thionchar a leathnú trí chaidreamh a chothú le 'daoine le seasamh'. Gairmiúlaigh a bhí i gceist aige leis an leagan seo. Ba chuid tábhachtach dá 'líonra', Cumann na nOistrí, grúpa príobháideach ina raibh acadúlaigh, maorlathaigh na Gaeilge, státsheirbhísigh, iriseoirí etc. páirteach. 'Fir le seasamh' amháin a bhíodh páirteach (bhí bac ar mhná, riail a chothaigh ráflaí mífholláine) i gcruinnithe de chuid an Chumainn, ag a mbíodh oistrí á n-alpadh, leann dubh á ól, agus smaointí agus cinní i leith pholasaithe na Gaeilge á bplé. Níor glacadh miontuairiscí.

Ar phléigh lucht Chumann na nOistrí moladh Ghaeil Bhaile Thormoid? Mo léan! Tá an t-aon duine a thabharfadh freagra cruinn ar an gceist seo ag tabhairt an fhéir le fada!

Seán Maguire

was born in Belfast and moved to Newry in the 1970s. He witnessed the extremities of political violence, a brother murdered during the conflict as well as several close friends. Seán left school at sixteen and worked in manual jobs before returning to education and obtaining various qualifications including a BA (Hons) in English Literature. His first poetry collection was *Harvest Soul* (Sessyu Press, 1998). In 2017 Seán published *For Those Left Behind*, a poetry collection steeped in political conflict. His work has featured in *Poetry in Motion*, nine muse poetry, *Honest Ulsterman*, *Pangolin Review* and *The Children of the Nation: An Anthology of Working People's Poetry from Contemporary Ireland* (Culture Matters, 2019).

Seán has worked in the voluntary sector since 1983, including Advice & Representation, Community and Youth Work, Training, and communications.

Window Pain

The noise of glass smashing against metal drew me to the living room window, through which I could see that a riot was unfolding forty yards from our front door. Two British army armoured cars were besieged by over thirty teenage boys, who pelted the military vehicles with bricks and bottles. One of the vehicles had broken down and the soldiers decided to wait inside until help arrived. The crowd grew in numbers and the ferocity of the riot increased. Suddenly there were loud bangs coming from both armoured cars and I saw puffs of white smoke emanating from little metal slats in both vehicles. Several rioters fell to the ground as rubber bullets pounded their lower limbs. Two young men arrived with a ladder—a stretcher substitute—and began to ferry their wounded friends to the relative safety of the opposite end of the street. The D.I.Y. stretcher-bearers were kept busy removing injured bodies during the riot.

The military vehicle, still in working order, let out merciful roars from its engine. The driver obviously applied his foot full on the accelerator to try and scare the young people. Every few minutes the armoured car went into reverse, braking suddenly after ten yards, and repeated the manoeuvre in a forward direction. The young rioters whistled and cheered as if they were at a stockcar rally. Suddenly, two separate groups of soldiers alighted from the armoured cars, brandishing riot shields and batons. Initially the young boys fired stones at the snatch squads, but they made a hasty retreat to the other end of the street when they realised the soldiers meant business. However, they ran into a trap and were met by a dozen soldiers, decked out in full riot gear, who arrived to provide support for their stricken colleagues. At least ten of the boys were captured and frog-marched past our house and made to squat on the ground beside the armoured cars with their hands placed firmly on their heads. The soldiers beat the boys with batons and pushed two of the oldest-looking youths on to the ground and began kicking them. Several women approached the soldiers remonstrating with them about the physical force applied, and judging by hand gestures from the soldiers it was clear they were not happy with the verbal riposte. The captured youths were taken into the next street from where they were put into jeeps and taken to a nearby British army base. I was glued to the window. Our street was bedlam; the riot was more exciting than any of the World War Two movies that routinely appeared on television.

My mum was in the scullery making dinner; she appeared to be aware of the riot, but did not take much notice as she was too busy cooking. She told me to stay away from the window in case the British soldiers mistook me for a gunman. She took a few steps into the living room whilst mashing a pot of potatoes and told me to sit down as a double bill of *Scooby Doo* cartoons was about to start on ITV. Although I was a big fan of the canine comic, the ongoing riot was more appealing. My mum returned to the kitchen and continued with preparing dinner. She repeated her warning about the window. This time her instructions were delivered with a higher and sterner tone. I took up position on the sofa and caught the last few minutes of *Scooby Doo*.

About twenty minutes went by and my mother, who was in full command of the scullery, began barking out orders about setting the dinner table. I extended two wings of a rickety Formica-coated table, placing assorted crockery and cutlery in a half orderly manner. My mum vacated the scullery and began pacing up and down the living room. She lit a cigarette and mumbled something about my oldest brother Frankie returning from a hurling match. Whilst the riot had reduced in scale to intermittent stone throwing, mainly towards the broken-down military vehicle, my mum was worried about my brother returning to the street whilst the situation was still volatile. I tried to comfort her by saying that Frankie probably called to granny's house as he usually did after home matches. A half hour and three cigarettes later my mum's anxiety was as high as a block of flats. No matter how many times I tried to reassure her about Frankie she blanked my interventions. She cursed the hurling club, the rioters, the British soldiers, and my father who was working in England.

I returned to the window as the house shook with the arrival of a large vehicle. It sounded like a big monster crawling towards wounded prey. I was disappointed; it was a recovery lorry accompanied by two jeeps. I was probably just as relieved as the soldiers, because as soon as their presence was no more my mum would hopefully calm down. A handful of soldiers had stayed behind to provide back up for their mates. It was a Friday evening; the illusive rioters were either in a queue at the local chippy or waiting to get their pay from fathers, older brothers or sisters returning home with weekly wage packets. I was bored and returned to the TV; *Blue Peter* had just started. I got up to switch channels in search of cartoons. *Top Cat* was on ITV. I curled up on the sofa to follow the exploits of 'TC' and 'Benny the Ball.' My mum had taken over my watch at the living room window. A noise rang out that sounded like gunfire. The next thing I knew she was roaring at the top of her voice, *'Oh, sweet Jesus, Holy Mary Mother of God! They have shot that wee boy.'*

I jumped up from the sofa and ran to my mother's side; she was pointing to the top end of the street where a young boy lay beside a bicycle. The boy appeared to be motionless and I could see blood pouring from his head. My mum wailed more religious references whilst throwing both arms in the air. She opened the front door and ran in the direction of the young boy. I followed suit, but I was stopped in my tracks by one of our neighbours who escorted me back towards our front door. Several women were standing in the middle of the road, some of them clutching rosary beads. A soldier knelt beside the boy; he had a green bag with a red cross on it and he was putting a bandage around the boy's head. Minutes later the soldier was joined by a local priest, Fr. Wilson, who knelt at the opposite side of the boy and appeared to be talking into one of his ears.

I looked towards the top of the street as loud voices increased in volume, adding to an already tense situation. A soldier was being guarded by two other military personnel. Apparently, he shot the boy at close range with a rubber bullet gun. The soldier had been disarmed. He cursed loudly and demanded to be released. A jeep pulled up and the soldier who did the shooting was whisked away. The women got closer to the boy and launched another round of prayers. Fr. Wilson held the boy's hands and blessed him. It was hard to see the boy's face as it was covered in blood and he was not easily recognisable from where I stood. My mother ran towards the female prayer group; she was shaking, crying, and stammering. Her words were unclear, but two of the women held her and were doing everything possible to calm her down. Then, I heard my mum screaming three words; three words that have been etched into my heart ever since: *'That's Michael McKenna'.* She repeated the words again: *'That's Michael McKenna.'* Her cries were unnerving, and she repeated the words again, adding that the wounded boy was our Frankie's best friend. A large British Army vehicle arrived; it had a big red cross painted on it. Fr. Wilson and two soldiers carried the wounded boy into the armoured car and its engine roared as it left the street for a short journey to the hospital.

My mum continued to roar and cry; she was inconsolable. Some of the women guided her to our windowsill and one of them lit a cigarette and gave it to her. She tried to smoke the cigarette, but her hands were shaking, and after another attempt she seemed content to let it fall to the ground. One of our neighbours, Mrs Donegan, called me over and asked me where Michael lived. I told her he lived two streets away. Mrs Donegan and a newly arrived young priest, Fr. Kearney, decided to go to the McKenna household to break the dreadful news about the shooting. Following a large mug of sweet tea, which smelt like whiskey, and two additional cigarettes, my mother returned to the house. She raised the possibility of making her way to my granny's house, but she abandoned the idea when I reminded her that Fr. Kearney said that the rioting had spread throughout the district.

One of our neighbours, Mrs Murphy, had just arrived home as things were dying down; once she heard about the incident she came to our house to comfort my mum. Mrs Murphy repeated some of the reassurances that I had issued earlier, although she got a better response. Mum continued to chain-smoke and pace about the house for another hour. In the meantime, Mrs Murphy put out dinner for me and continued to provide moral support. There was a loud knock at our front door. My mum froze and looked towards me, fear written boldly across her tearful face. She blessed herself and looked towards Mrs Murphy, who slowly opened the door. Frankie entered the living room with our uncle Billy. My mum ran to my brother before he spoke a word, hugging him and sobbing. Kind Mrs Murphy joined in the hugging before leaving. Billy was a taxi driver and the only member of the family circle who had a car. He explained to my mum that he collected Frankie from my granny's house when the word came through that the rioting had stopped. Frankie, as I expected, went to my granny's house after the hurling match. Our grandparents would not let him go home until the trouble had ceased. My mum hugged Frankie again and, as her face met mine, I could see a river of tears streaming down the back of Frankie's coat. She sat Frankie down on an armchair. She was tearful but had somehow managed to compose herself to break the news about Michael. We had since learnt that Michael had died in the hospital. When my mum told Frankie about what happened to Michael, he looked at her and went quiet. His face was snow white and his whole body shivered. His defiant stare couldn't conceal his emotions. It was obvious Frankie was upset and angry.

Uncle Billy hugged Frankie and told him how sorry he was about Michael. Billy left and there were just the three of us, a trinity of sadness and despair. Michael had been in our house the day before, joking with Frankie and my mum about a TV programme called *The Jimmy Young Show*. Now this twelve-year-old boy was laid out in a hospital mortuary, his head blown apart by a rubber bullet. Michael was riding a bike on his way to collect his father's best suit from the pawnshop. Michael's parents were due to go to a family wedding the next day.

I went to bed in tears, confused, frightened and angry. I was ten years of age, two years younger than Michael. I just could not take it in. My mum told me to say a prayer for Michael. I did, even though I did not understand what God could do. I did not sleep much that night. I kept wakening up and thinking about Michael and Frankie playing hurling matches, and chasing me away any time I tried to tag along with them. There were sporadic riots throughout the night and gun battles between the IRA and British soldiers raged into the dying embers of a solemn day.

Saturday morning arrived in a haze. It was usually the highlight of the week, with a range of TV programmes to watch, accompanied by bottles of lemonade and chocolate biscuits. I could not bring myself to watch TV or eat breakfast and did not give the treats a second glance. Frankie lay on the sofa, pretending to be asleep, but steady trickles of emotion rained down his face telling the true story. My mum said the morning news was full of reports about Michael being killed, and the British soldier who shot him was taken off duty and he was being sent back to his barracks in England. My mum was angry and said that the soldier would get off scot-free just like the ones who shot thirteen people in Derry. Later that day, as we walked behind Michael's funeral from the hospital to his home, we both hoped that the soldier would rot in hell. Frankie said he wished he were older so that he could get a gun and shoot the soldier who killed his best friend.

Later that evening my mum took Frankie to Michael's house. After he saw Michael lying in a coffin with a bandaged head he ran home and went straight up to our bedroom, crying loudly for hours until he fell asleep. Hundreds of people attended Michael's funeral; his classmates walked behind the hearse in full school uniform, and his hurling club jersey straddled a white coffin. Michael's mother collapsed at the graveside and had to receive medical treatment.

The soldier who shot Michael was brought to court two years after the killing and was acquitted and returned to his British Army regiment. The McKenna family were given £150 in compensation for their dead son. Under the law, that was all a dead child was worth. Despite the passing of time, Frankie and I talk about Michael, and our hearts still weigh heavy for the tragic loss of our friend. We wonder if Michael were still alive would he have got married and had kids just like us. It is likely that the soldier who shot him went on to have a family. I hoped this soldier had a son and maybe, just maybe, on this boy's twelfth birthday he had the courage to say, 'Son, I have something to tell you. I once killed a child your age.'

Maeve McKenna

is originally from Dublin, Ireland. She grew up with her parents, five siblings, a dog, two budgies and a goldfish in a three bed terraced house in Cabra. Maeve has worked at various jobs over the years and wrote in her spare time. She moved to rural Sligo in 2001 with her husband and three children. She writes more regularly now while also working to fund her children's third-level education. Her work has been published in print and online. She is currently focusing on completing her first collection of poetry.

I Want To Go Home

I want Casey's manged, flea-infested mongrel to chase me as far as O'Dwyer's unhinged gate, mother waiting on the doorstep, smoke from a *Silk Cut*, red issuing like language from her lips, the father educated by the *Evening Press* crossword, my sister in casualty. I want my brothers wedged against venetian blinds, when headlocks are conversations, and my favourite dead aunt buying greasy takeaways to help my mother.

I want the 22A bus to Cabra rattling inside my bones, lungs wheezing inside the fumes of Poolbeg towers. I want street signs vandalised with paint, chewing gum strewn footpaths and a wheel-less bike, locked to a railway fence. I want buildings of two-up, two-down, crow-stalked chimneys, smog, heat bouncing grey mist off concrete, high-rise skylines, piss-stained lanes and the stench of the low tide Liffey in my nostrils.

I want the squeal of street cats mating on broken bottle-topped walls, wood chip crates of Jaffa oranges at 5 a.m. in the fruit markets, stacked like a Southsider's tree-house, high heels of fearless youth on cobblestones in Smithfield, Croke Park and the Dubs defeated. I want kids skidding on amber oak leaves on O'Connell Street, The Oarsman early house with watery Guinness heads, Leeson Strip on New Year's Eve, rancid wine and drug-fuelled dancing.

I want the aloofness of Clerys' window display, Moore Street traders, the threat of severed fish-heads in a pram and mouldy water in the cross at The Garden of Remembrance. I want old women battering rugs on washing lines, Glasnevin's withered wreaths, bonfires melting power lines, the risky Phoenix Park at dusk, my father downing pints of slop at closing time in the Five Lamps every Saturday night.

I want The Beehive newsagents to sell one more loose fag, Stein's butchers a pound of offal. I want trees fenced-off over tarmac pavements, the ominous church, barbed wire school railings and the beatings.

I want Erris Road, white, weather-glazed front door with yellow daffodils in stained glass circles, one mildewed toilet, a dilapidated kitchenette and geezer moist windows, the shadow of grandfathers in suits hung inside frames in the narrow hallway.

I want nicotine-laced curtains, the smell of cabbage, twin-tub flushing last night's vomit from sheets, final reminders unopened on the door-mat, a scraggy Christmas tree at a tilt on the beige shag-pile carpet. I want orange ropes knotted to poles, wooden pegs with wire knuckles clinging to bell-bottom jeans as they swing wildly over the neighbour's breeze block wall. I want the bag of Willie Quigley's new-season spuds turning to seed in the shed beside the litter of abandoned kittens.

I want my mother's slap, father's pen, my sister crying on the top bunk, my brother's bruised eye-socket. I want the bones of my first dog buried in the back garden.

Victoria McNulty

is a poet and writer from the East End of Glasgow. Victoria's maternal family emigrated from Ulster to Glasgow to work as coopers and factory labourers in the North and East End of the city. Like many Glaswegians she is proud of the valuable contribution they made to Scotland's cultural fabric and maintains close ties with Ireland. Her heartfelt and authentic work focuses on working-class experiences and Irish heritage in the city. Her debut pamphlet 'Confessionals' was published in 2017 by Speculative Books, and her writing features in Neu! Reekie!, Nutmeg and The Joe Strummer Foundation. She has performed at arts events across the UK and Ireland, including the Edinburgh Fringe, BBC Music Festival, Féile an Phobail (Belfast) and the James Connolly Festival (Dublin).

White Horses

In 1995, you would pull fags from a green and white packet, with cabbage slurped on the stove. Your ubiquitous potatoes boiling ever truculent. At teatime, we would push them round our plates as a family. I would stab them with a fork in your distraction, hold them to my eyeline and try to watch *Brookside* through the membranes, only to pop them in my mouth as the gaze of rage descended. These were our best days. I loved every inch of you as you puffed Consulates in the kitchen, with an ever brew of strong black tea. Adorned in a cleaner's apron, though you didn't seem to work. We would flick magazines you'd bought me, Gallagher brothers on every page. 'So handsome,' you'd say, 'Black Irish,' like it was a matter of fact. As smoke plumed from flaky lips, you'd paint pictures of your father, settled as a pauper in Glasgow's Garngad, his strong jaw and stern temperament. How with a drink in him he'd terrorise you, as Irish men often do. You'd confide how you'd wished you'd taken him home before he died. To taste the salt air and touch the Ulster soil. Still, we never talked about Ireland in our house. Not really. When white heat ripped a bomb through the *Six O'Clock News*. Twisted metal and zombies walking with bleeding-headed hysteria, shocked and destitute. When ambulances and stretchers scattered the charred precincts, Queen's English accents shaping their usual excuses of 'incendiary devices, escalation and retaliation.' You sat static in your favourite chair, raised yourself, cough-hobbled to the telly and switched it off at the wall. 'The IRA are killing ordinary people now,' you wheezed. Only now I understand that you were too crestfallen to look.

When you died, I looked for you, filling the blanks with books. The first woman in my family to get a university degree, I devoured four years of Ulster Cycles, place names and protests. I searched for your remains in the paragraphs and page breaks. Spotlit in dusty libraries, I'd let my digits dance the cheekbones of old photographs, trying to touch some semblance of you.

I could exist in these margins, but it wasn't where I belonged. So most weekends I would march our old stomping grounds, Gallowgate through the Calton, green and white scarfed, surrounded by men. Their hands and voices hoarse from building site roars, bow-legged, their eyes a wild sparkle like yours. I'd hold my drunk chin high and my insides would rise as the stadium came into sight. As the shoal swelled, a tin whistle would herald us past the Jock Stein stand, milk fingers pouring a slow rendition of 'The Leaving of Liverpool'. It rose with a heat of fried onions and police horse shite in the ether. In the pub, we would warm with stories from a land that was not our home and an aching that Scotland wasn't either. We sat squished, comfortably, thigh to thigh, knee to knee. Punters would duck behind tables at the ring of a phone, fearful it was their girlfriend calling from home. In the calm of our storm old men would drip water into drams, heat hands on unlit fires as their wives cooed a tune. Swaying tipsily, sequined and glittered with floral perfume, their rough diamond glamour always reminded me of you. Yet, as our city changed, their serenade faded too. My wildness tamed as I grew. I gave birth to a Scottish son with an Irish name and a heart-shaped face like yours. For hours he would sit on my knee, adored, soothed to melancholic songs from rebel mouths while I knitted him stories about my Gran.

Of an autumn, we retraced the steps you never got to take, now living more comfortably than you ever could. My son and I wandered Derry's walls, spying murals on their tourist trails. Artist impression Armalites fired his wee boy mind as he sucked on hard boiled sweets, and sponged second-hand bias from my understanding. In a museum, we held our gasps in tight, frown-browed, in a ribbon of silence. A glass-cased rubber bullet shot at a child just his age. An unnamed soldier. A trite Tory apology. These people were the same class as us, ablaze like me and tied to you. It seemed so cruel. Still, to see the world through the eyes of a tourist is a privileged thing. By evening, we visited my son's first pub in good spirits. Oak tables and etched glass partitions, stale with booze, newspapers stuffed in the corners. A hurl nailed to the wall. Captivated, my boy perched a chipped stool, a cocky barman regaling him with proud stories of broken noses and solid balls. As he listened, his tiny fingers dripped stout from my half pint into our dog's mouth. Her gums slobbering lustily as the iron coated her tongue, old men buying them both bags of crisps for their troubles.

Despite your city dwellings you were, by nature, a water lover, although you were too scared to swim. Summers on the Isle of Bute fondly sepia-stamped in our family's collective memory. Tins of pictures are scattered with younger you, showing leg, leather-tanned at fountain. Geraniums and marigolds spilling a rainbow from the flower beds. You said you loved the ocean most when the white horses roamed. In my memory you would stand primal, face first, sea spray sinking into your worry wrinkles. Hood up, swallowed by the ocean that tied your roots together. This was heaven to you, growing up ragged in the city soot, sharing beds with siblings, toilets with your neighbours. To be alone in nothingness, in the moment. Your winter years were spent cough-broken in an East End scheme, its breeze blocks foreign to coastal dampness. When I came along, the water that had once brought needed isolation, built bridges when you needed them. On our kitchen days, you'd talk of the Giant's Causeway, stocked with recollections, half-truths and fantasies. I'd warriors dressed like babies. Giants building mono-blocked patios from Ireland to Glasgow. I'm sure you embellished somewhat, as you always did. It was always a pleasure to heed you talk pish. How you revelled in the moment.

This is how we chose to embellish you, by the coast on the honeycomb causeway of a shoreline you had never returned to, but always wanted to. The blues and browns of Ireland lapping round our feet, golden orange crisp in the horizon. There was a midsummer tinge to the autumn air as we stood, fingers interlocked, our pooch mooching through bubble seaweed, tourists scaling the peaks behind us. In just one moment I breathed you in, saltwater building in my eyes; I wiped them dry, crouched and dipped fingers below the stained-glass windows of the ocean church, its water pirouetting my hands in the undertow. As I exhaled, coldness enveloping my bit nails and nipped cuts, I felt a bit of you there. Swallowed as you once were, standing in the face of the ocean spray.

It's been twenty-five years since we spoke, smoke-shrouded in your industrious kitchen, coughs and cooking lacing the stove-warmed air. I'm still writing to you. Still seeing you in every page, tripping over you in every cracked pavement. I was wrong to rummage for you in the past, as I suspect you would have told me so. You see, you were never lost to me. I had to extend my arms to Ireland. I journeyed the choppiest of seas, to taste the beauty and bitterness of a country misplaced to find you as you were. Both glamourous and broken, twisted and loving, sat chimney-smoking in our soup pot scullery. Yet, I never once recognised my searching as grief. Now I see you lived in my story all along. May you always reside in my pages.

Bernadette Murphy

lives in her adopted County Galway. She works as a nurse and as an essential worker worked throughout the lockdown.

Bernadette was born into a working-class family many decades ago and has worked since she was eighteen, often combining it with study. She has a bachelor's degree, which she underwent while raising her twins.

She believes the working class are the backbone of every country.

She has been writing creatively, on and off, since a young lady and enjoys keeping diaries detailing her personal journey through unusual events.

Dear Diary is a combination of entries from her diary written during the COVID-19 pandemic.

Dear Diary

May 25th 2020

There have been no COVID-19 related deaths today, this is the first time since March 21st the 'R' (reproductive COVID-19 rate) is between 0.4 and 0.6.

We can be joyful, hopeful even.

We've now had seven weeks of sunshine with very little rain—this is unusual for April/May in Ireland.

We can be thankful, happy even.

Today I'm counting my blessings while accepting my lot—a trait I associate with my working class status!

I think of previous generations and what they survived, the famine, two World Wars, emigration, TB, polio...

There is a slower pace to everything these days as the battle with COVID-19 transmission continues, shutting down to slow the spread. There is a new quieter lifestyle.

The roads to and from work are quieter, fewer cars, people working from home, workplaces closed, the high-risk groups self-isolating and those over seventy cocooning in their homes. There are fewer planes in the sky, pollution generally reduced.

There is an increase in cyclists, walkers and joggers, lovely to see whole families out walking in the country lanes. I feel the rhythm of the country air has a calming effect in communities shadowed in darkness.

People ask:

'What is the first thing you will do when the restrictions are lifted?'

'Where is the first place you will go?'

I believe that post lockdown we will have an opportunity to do things differently and maybe better.

I've worked throughout the lockdown. I'm working class; as a nurse

I'm described as an essential worker. I'm a professional working-class person —part of that frontline so widely talked about in the media.

I'm fortunate in that my children are adults now. Some of my colleagues are using their annual leave entitlement to care for their children with schools and crèches closed and grandparents cocooning.

Work is difficult, challenging, guidelines change frequently. Wearing PPE in the sunshine is uncomfortable. There is an absence of families/visitors to comfort patients/residents.

I have 'a permission slip' from my employer stating I can move/drive for my work outside of the two kilometre from home restriction, on May 5th this restriction was changed to five kilometres.

I'm proud to be working class. I value myself, flaws and all! I don't see myself as a 'wage slave', more as part of an ordinary class doing extraordinary things. Being working class is complex.

What do we mean by working class?

Implicit in everything concerning people is a set of assumptions about the way people should be. It's difficult to explain how we are, much more than how we are perceived. I suppose we must be participants in something in order to understand and be proud. A sort of shared experience. Being working class to me means being educated with an opinion on everything!

Do we have power? Do I want to have power over others, seeing that one of the reasons (in my humble opinion) most wars were waged was to gain power over other people? I would much prefer to have insight and sensitivity to issues of justice.

There is a grittiness to the working class that makes us 'get up, dress up and show up'. We get on with things, do what has to be done unapologetically, often with a twinkle in our eye! Can this be attributed to our past, our history or to our journey so far?

I believe there is a rebellious streak in us, which may hint that we do indeed live in the shadow of our past.

Staying in the present moment, I'm proud to be working class. After all, working outside of the home was an opportunity denied to my mother and grandmother!

'Till next time...

B.

David Murphy

has had six books published, most recently *Drowning in the Desert*, his first poetry collection, brought out by Revival Press in 2020. One of his main concerns is inequality in society, a theme familiar to him from growing up in Cork in the 1960s right through to present-day Ireland. This theme echoes in much of his work, including 'Token House' which is set in an imaginary Dublin where inequality is taken to the extreme. Visit his website at www.davidmurph.wordpress.com

Token House

Lumen pulled on the choke and revved the throttle. The Volkswagen Beetle shugged on the upslope from the basement parking space on the corner of Ailesbury Road. He leaned over the steering wheel, face inches from the windshield, as if that might urge the car up and prevent the rear-mounted engine from becoming a dead weight to drag the car down again. The VW inched up to street level, and the usual unruly mob of local school kids were waiting to taunt him.

As soon as they caught sight of who sat behind the wheel, they jeered with that familiar chant: 'Lumen, Lumen, where are all the Jewmen?'

He kept his foot on the accelerator, telling himself these were just satchel-wearing children out of kindergarten. They didn't know the gravity of their jeering, unlike secondary school kids who chanted worse things about death camps and Final Solutions and threw mud at him on wet days. Lumen had glanced at his watch before setting out. The older ones would not gather for another hour, thank goodness. Best get back to Token House before they arrive. Better not run over any little ones, he thought, as the car lurched forward. As soon as he pulled beyond the gate, the children shrieked and stepped back in mock terror. The echoes of their chanting faded in his ears: 'Lumen, Lumen, king of all the Jewmen.'

His Beetle blended in with other VWs going into town, most of them produced in the *Vorsprung* assembly plant on Dublin's Northside. Not one was driven by a Jew, except the one Lumen sat in now. He kept his eyes on the road, avoiding stares of pedestrians who recognised him. Traffic slowed, forcing him to stop on the bridge. A woman strode into the middle of the road. She paused and stood in front of the bonnet. Hands on hips, shopping bags dangling, a 'well now, what have we here?' look in her eyes. Lumen was used to that look. It was not just his religion and race etched on his face—he bore that bewildered gaze which betrayed the mental frailty that was with him always: the dim, gormless look of the intellectually challenged. The woman did not sneer at the simpleton behind the wheel. She eyed him pitifully and walked on.

*

Fifty-five minutes later Lumen parked his car at the servants' entrance of Token House and checked his watch: one minute past four. He carried in a box of groceries.

Tilda was delighted to see what sat on top of the onions. 'Where did you get that orange?' she squealed in disbelief.

'Rationing is being lifted on some luxury items, though still only one per household.'

'Oh.'

Lumen shared Tilda's instant deflation. One per household meant the orange would go upstairs with the 6.30 dinner trays. He helped her unload the box, knowing she never used the full version of her name, Matilda. She hated to be called Matt or Mattie. Lumen knew those to be masculine names, not a woman's. 'Kids calling you 'Mattie' again today?' he ventured.

'It's not that. They always do that.' Tilda paused at the scullery entrance, carrots hanging from one hand, bag of apples in the other. 'Frau Schweinsteiger rang just after you left. We have a private tour coming in at five.'

Lumen pulled the watch out of his waistcoat pocket and scratched his scalp—a minute over fifty to get the place ready.

Schweinsteiger swanned into the basement, guests trailing behind her. She ignored Lumen and Tilda, swivelled like a ballerina, her flurry of arms encompassed the kitchen and everything in it as though there were no difference between servant and stove. 'This is the way things used to be in the Fatherland,' she addressed the guests. 'Undesirables like these two often worked downstairs. Even model families employed them. Imagine!'

Lumen let her words flow through the cellar skylight. He and Tilda stood by the wall as they always did at tour time. His eyes took in the guests. A family of six, including mother and father, all wearing Irish-German People's Front badges on their lapels. They bore that unmistakable country look. *A smell of hay off them,* Lumen had heard Dubliners joke about country folk. This amused him until the father, a thick-set, gruff-looking yokel if ever there was one, took the pipe out of his mouth and demanded, 'Why isn't that young man wearing a yellow star?'

Lumen felt the breath catch in his throat. He wanted to hide his reddening cheeks with his hands.

'There is no need,' said Schweinsteiger. 'He's the only Jew left in your capital city. Everyone knows his face—the most notorious twenty-one-year-old in Dublin. The days of the yellow star are over. We keep these two here as an example of what can happen. Undeterred and unculled, they would breed like rats and insinuate themselves into households, even in the most salubrious districts of your country.'

Suddenly, the countrywoman spoke. 'They look after the kitchen well.' She had been running a finger over the surfaces, the cleanliness testimony to Lumen and Tilda's frantic scrubbing of the previous hour.

The man turned with the look of a husband who urgently needed to put his wife in place. Schweinsteiger got in first, as was her custom. 'This pair have been well trained, but they are taking the jobs of two Irish people who could ...' The tour guide let her words trail, distracted by the youngest of her visiting group. The boy of about nine had begun to giggle loudly. 'What do you find so amusing, little man?' Schweinsteiger asked.

The boy continued to giggle. He was pointing at Tilda.

'Jesus, Mary and Joseph!' The wife's attention was not on the cleanliness of the kitchen now. She cupped her chin in her hands. 'Excuse us. Paudie's not used to seeing ... people of colour.'

'Don't worry, my little man.' Schweinsteiger interjected more firmly this time. 'There is no need for discipline. No one apologises for laughing at a mere negress.'

Lumen glanced sideways. He sensed Tilda's embarrassment and felt her anger in waves.

'We are now going upstairs. Do not salute the servants; they are not proper citizens. Come, let's go. The model family awaits—a fine Aryan looking couple with two delightful children, all blonde hair and blue eyes.' Schweinsteiger ruffled her hands a little too vigorously through the nine-year-old boy's head of reddish hair.

Lumen and Tilda watched the last of the family exit the kitchen. He checked his watch and said. 'Fourteen minutes past five; just over an hour to get dinner ready.' He lifted a saucepan off a wall-hook.

'Best get cracking then!' Tilda attacked the nearest carrot as though it were a serpent doomed to die by a hundred vicious cuts.

Lumen could tell she was still annoyed hours later as they finished washing up. To cheer her up, he put on his best mock-Dublin accent: 'That family the Frau brought in had a right smell of hay off them.'

'Oh, Lu—you make me laugh, despite your ridiculous fixations, especially your constant watch-checking.'

He smiled. He hated when people were unhappy.

Tilda still looked pre-occupied. 'I don't think they'll let us stay here much longer,' she ventured.

A sudden hollowness gnawed into Lumen's stomach. 'What makes you say that, Tilda?'

'They have token houses, with model families and pairs of servants like us, in other cities in Britain and the continent, but they're replacing the undesirables.'

'How do you know that?' Lumen felt the urge to put his hand in his pocket and run his fingers around the rim of his grandfather's watch.

'Somebody taunted me about it on Grafton Street this morning.'

'They're always taunting us. How can you bear to go out?'

She handed him the last of the saucers to dry.

Rows of trenches furrowed Lumen's brow. He placed the saucer in the cupboard and closed the door. 'How can they replace us? There are no other Jews or negroes in Dublin.'

'Haven't you seen Al Jolson in the picture house? Lots of white actors play black minstrels. What's to stop an actress putting boot polish on her face and pretending to be me? Course, they could replace me with a homosexual, just to vary the undesirables a bit.' Lumen watched Tilda fold her arms across her big, broad chest. She continued: 'Course, they'd have no bother getting an actor to play your part. Jews look like every other white person—well, most of 'em, anyway.'

Lumen wanted to take the watch out of his pocket to read again the wording of his grandfather's retirement inscription, which he read several times a day. Tilda had already given out to him for fixations so he contented himself with squeezing his hand around it. She walked to the stove. Turning, she said, 'Grab a plate. Time for our din-dins now. Lu, don't look so sad! They won't come for you. They'll always keep a token Jew. It's me ...' Her voice faltered... 'They might take me. Don't cry, Lu. They...it's just a rumour about negroes being removed from the token houses all over Europe. Seemingly we're surplus now.' She paused, knowing her use of big words would have the desired effect; his flow of tears stopped as he tried to figure out her meaning. 'Will everything be okay, Tildas?' he pleaded, using the plural of her name as he always did when frightened or worried.

'Yes, of course, that's what I meant; everything will be fine.'

Unable to resist any longer, Lumen pulled out the watch. 'Just after a quarter to eight,' he confirmed. 'An hour and a half before we begin to get their supper ready.'

'Lu!' Tilda's burly shoulders throbbed with laughter. 'You're such a pain!'

He again checked the time in ambient light that streamed through his narrow window. A quarter past midnight. Silvery light was made one part of streetlamps, two parts stars. He could see his favourite constellation. *Draw a line across Orion's belt*, Grandfather had told him in the long ago. *Extend that line seven times to arrive at* ... Aldebaran! Bright and shiny like a jewel in the sky. Lumen wondered if it was possible to go there—rumours said the Germans had rockets that could go all the way into the sky.

He wondered if camps existed in the vicinity of Aldebaran, which made him think about the Curragh Camp in Kildare. That place was full of tinkers and lunatics from the asylums. He shivered—remembering how he had nearly been put in an asylum in early childhood. His family insisted on teaching him at home in their tiny house in Jewtown, the Albert Road area of Cork. He shivered even more when he thought of that other camp, Spike Island, where he had spent much of 1947 and most of '48. He had been there when they started to build the smokestacks. 'To keep you all warm this winter,' the camp commandant quipped with a harsh laugh Lumen would never forget. When Lumen won the camp lottery in the autumn of '48, the Jews all laughed, too. 'What a specimen to represent us,' they sniggered. They envied him for winning the only prize—a one-way ticket from Spike back to the mainland and a life of servitude in Token House. Some prisoners claimed the draw was rigged so that a simpleton would win. 'A perfect choice to represent his race,' the commandant announced over the camp's PA system, with another harsh laugh, on the day of Lumen's release back into the world.

He never saw Grandfather or his family again, or any other descendants of the once proud Lithuanians who had settled near the banks of the river in Cork in the last half of the nineteenth century. The German collaborators billeted Lumen for one night in McCurtain Street near the station so he could catch the first train for Dublin next morning.

He took one last lingering look at Aldebaran, turned in the bed and made himself think of Tilda. He heard her gentle snores, her headboard just behind his wall. He pictured her big, broad shoulders—so strong yet fragile —she was like a new mother to him. With that thought he was back with his old family again and he cried even more. The last time he checked his watch the dial showed half past two. Sleep came. Sometime around three, the tracks of his tears dried on the pillow.

A screech of brakes jolted him off his mattress. He jerked his feet onto the bedroom floor, startled as much by the noise as the earliness of the day. He checked his watch: half past six—dawn. By the time he got to the window, the tailboard of the truck was down and another sound filled his ears—the thud of jackboot on concrete.

He had no time to get dressed. Sounds came from Tilda's room. He heard her door creak open. He ran out of his room and stood facing her in his pyjamas. Lumen had never seen her like this, standing on the wooden floor of the corridor, her eyes two bowls brimming over. This was so unlike her—she had never wept in all the months he had been here. He had never seen her look so frightened. 'Tildas!' he cried. 'What's happening?'

The SS man took the stairs three at a time. Lumen could smell the hay off him—a local recruit, the worst sort—so Tilda had told him once in a quiet moment in the kitchen. Lumen saw the glare in the officer's eyes as he brushed him aside, and heard the boots of other soldiers on the stairs. He wanted to scream and cover his eyes and ears with his hands, and he could have, because they had no interest in him. The SS officer took hold of Tilda, manhandling her to the head of the stairs where two soldiers grabbed her. The last thing Lumen saw of Tilda was the panic in her big round eyes, and the last she heard of him was his voice: 'Tildas, Tildas! Why are they taking you away?'

Frank Murphy

is working-class. He left school at thirteen and returned to education at his own expense, studying telecommunications because a book in the local library made him curious about how transformers worked. He got into writing 'by accident' when unable to enrol in a Dunshaughlin computer course, as it was full. The woman at the desk suggested a free writing course instead.

Frank satirises the class realities of Ireland. Winner of The Jonathan Swift Creative Writing Award/Poetry 2009. Shortlisted and placed in many others, including Listowel (Humorous Essay 2017). Also Swords and the Jonathan Swift 2017. Others going back include the Oliver Goldsmith, Francis Ledwidge, Dromineer, Boyle. Most recent shortlisted Tralee Humorous Verse 2019 and commended Jonathan Swift 2019.

Frank worked at just about everything, and knows this is no country to end up on the wrong side of.

Welcome to Dystopia

(Another Handmaid's Tale)

Please note that your calls may be recorded for training and quality purposes, so listen carefully before selecting any of the following options, as all of our operators are busy as we're experiencing a high volume of calls.

Though alternatively you could text us without incurring any extra costs; unless you're dialling from a mobile, in which case please stay on the line and one of our operators will be with you shortly. There are no free lunches!

We are also available via the worldwide web, if you could afford us, or that you can prove that you're not a robot. To continue...

For fake news: dial one.

For anyone who might be bugging you: dial two.

For those of you who eat your dinner in the middle of the day: dial three.

For a ringing endorsement on dietary supplements: dial four.

For an approximation or estimation on what could be construed as strict rotation or slow progress: dial five.

For the criminal injuries compensation tribunal: dial six.

For an engaged-tone: dial seven.

For paperless billing on all of the above: dial eight.

For a supplementary benefit, or the budgetary estimates, or for any information on how you can report on an unlicensed locksmith, you can dial nine.

For disturbance money, if you happen to be a member of the Permanent Government, you can dial any number you like, but if you'd like to hear this message again in any meaningful context that doesn't require a herd number or a plastic tag in your ear, preferably yellow... Well we're working on it!

The background music you've just been listening to is part of our composition program and is subject to copyright, though you can download a sample, provided that you include a copy of the Nursing Home Shuffle or the Blue Bottle Blues, courtesy of the Fair Deal Scheme. We'll be celebrating the launch of our CD any day now, eff off!

If you or anyone you know has been affected by any of these issues, or is subject to domestic abuse or violence, you could try.... beep beep beep beep beep beep...

Alan O' Brien

is a bricklayer by trade, raised in the Finglas/Ballymun area of Dublin. In opposition to *emigration culture*, returned to education in 2011, receiving a BA in English/History at UCD, 2015. Also the Dublin City Lord Mayor's Certificate in Oral History 2016. Shortlisted for the Maeve Binchy Travel Award 2015; was winner of the P.J. O'Connor Award 2016, and finalist for the Lingo Spoken Word festival 2016. He has been published in *Rabble* magazine, *Travellers' Voice* publications co-wrote, directed, and performed in a play entitled *From the Backbone Out*, performed Liberty Hall, Dublin, 2016 and 2017. Poems included in *The Children of the Nation: An Anthology of Working People's Poetry from Contemporary Ireland* (Culture Matters, 2019).

Co-directed and performed in a dramatic poetical showcase entitled, *Seven Ages: Like It or Not*, in Smock Alley Theatre, Dublin, February 2020. Poems included in American poetry anthology entitled *Home Anthology: an antidote of expression*, edited by Michael Guinn, 2020.

Culture

The smattering of rain had deluged into a torrential downpour splattering the pavement just as Tony Ennis ducked in through the front doors to the lounge of The Penthouse pub. He thanked 'Jaysus' as he slipped off his brown leather jacket and checked out his new sky-blue Ben Sherman shirt and black Diesel jeans, ensuring all was still pristine. Satisfied that he was in actual fact, pristine, Tony winked at himself in the reflection of a door panel window and opened the inner door to the lounge.

A rumbling cacophony of conversation, laughs, shouts and whispers surrounded the young man as he entered into a huge crowd of literally wall-to-wall punters. The Penthouse was unusually busy for a Wednesday evening, the reason becoming apparent to Tony as he noticed an abundance of Travellers standing at and around the bar. There had been a funeral for one in their community.

Tony had heard of this bereavement a couple of days before. Paudge Ward it was who had died. A Traveller, who was known and trusted by a good percentage of the Ballymun population because of his vast equine knowledge and skill. If someone's horse was poorly or needed attention it was Paudge they always sought out. His advice was classed as golden. But he had died at the ripe old age (for a Traveller man) of sixty-seven, of what exactly Tony didn't hear when he was told the news.

His dark-blue eyes scanned the bubbling human swell that filled the great oblong expanse of The Penthouse in search of the friends he had arranged to meet there. With no success, Tony took out his phone and opened the inbox of his text messages.

'The seats down the back beside the jax,' he read.

He slipped the phone back into his jeans' pocket, and jostled and slid through the hodgepodge crowd, apologising and excusing himself, and sporadically winking a nod in recognition to the punters he knew.

'Story, Ennis?!' came a shout over the din from Tony's side, his head snapping around and face smiling in recognition at the cluster of faces known to him. It was Tomo Layden and Deckie Fleming and Big Paulie Boland.

Tomo and Deckie were great little horse enthusiasts in their day. They had two excellently kept horses that Paudge had advised them with. Then their horses were impounded and sold on immediately—to those who were in possession of stables. The boys had subsequently fallen foul of boredom and experimentation and had ended up addicts. It was rare to see them in the pub. But this was Paudge's funeral.

And Paulie had been a horse owner when he was younger, but sold her a few years ago, as he was working flat-out on the sites and hadn't the time to give her. It broke his heart to sell her, but Paudge had made sure she got a decent owner.

'Just saying to the boys, did you see Dixie Nolan flew in for the funeral?' Paulie said loudly.

'Who, the jockey?!' Tony replied.

'The very one, got up and spoke on the altar an' all!'

'No way, I didn't know he knew Paudge Ward?' Tony quizzed.

'Knew?!' laughed Paulie, taking a gulp of his stout. Licking his upper lip, he said: 'According to Dixie Nolan, Paudge Ward was the very reason he took an interest in horses in the first place. How he showed him how to love and respect the animals, had an understandin' of them. He started getting upset an' all, saying Paudge was a father figure to him and to loadsa others whose fathers were anything but. It was lovely, now, has-to-be-said.'

'Ah it was, it was lovely it was. Wasn't it, Deckie?' drawled Tomo.

'It was, yeah, lovely it was. He's from Finglas he is, Dixie Nolan is,' said Deckie as if waking from a snooze. The Valium he had taken to get him through the funeral (before he could find a spot and turn-on for the day) had kicked in properly, and he was coasting, for now.

The general small-talk and platitudes that such occasions call for, were distributed between the four before Tony broke away to continue his search. As luck would have it he seen Gringo's big head, bobbling over the heads of some other punters at the bar, the red flash of his hair like a beacon in the fog.

'Gringo!' Tony called.

Gringo's redhead snapped around as he rose on his toes and spied over the crowd. On seeing Tony he let out a shrill whistle and raised his hand, pointing to where he and the girls were seated. Tony made his way to where he pointed, reaching a small table with the two dolled-up-to-the-nines girls,

Deborah and Josie, sitting drinking G&T's.

'Lookin' smashing, *a cailíní*,' yodelled a smiling Tony as he bent to kiss his girlfriend, Deborah.

'Howaya babe, here's a stool,' said Deborah, smacking Tony with her lips and sliding a concealed stool from under the table.

'That's my woman.' Tony winked and sat down, allowing himself to be again slightly amazed at the excellence of Deborah, his girl.

'Have ya chosen yer winnin' song for tonight?' chirped Josie, excitedly.

Tonight was The Penthouse Grand Finale Karaoke Night, with a €500 prize for first place. It was hotly contested, with singers coming from places as far as Tallaght and even from Ballybrack to compete. The standard was always of the highest form.

Tony was an excellent singer; Dean Martin and Burt Bacharach songs being his favourites, especially Bacharach.

'I was thinking "Eye of the Tiger",' Tony replied.

'Fuck-off! *Eye of the* bleedin' *Tiger*, d'ya hear him?!' Josie giggled while nudging her friend.

'He was sayin' he's goin' to do something *special*,' Deborah informed Josie, 'something we wouldn't expect from him. Aren't ya?' she giggled, with a hot-electrical flash in her eye.

'I was sayin' that, and I am doin' that, but, I'm keepin' it as a surprise...'

'Aye aye, saveloy!' sang Gringo, as he arrived to the table with new G&T's and pints for them—all skilfully grappled between his two hands—just as Josie was asking Tony what it was he was planning to sing at the *finale* for the thirty-seventh time.

Placing the glasses into the centre of the table, Gringo sat down and leaned back on the stool and viewed Tony while inhaling deeply through his nostrils, widening his bright blue eyes in the process, running his fingers through his red hair and confirming to Tony that he had just taken part in the consumption of cocaine.

'I see we have some caravan-dwellers with us tonight,' began Gringo, looking around the bar with the bravado of a *cock-of-the-walk*. Then, smirking, he ducked his head into Tony and the girls and said, 'Here, what key can open any lock?'

'Shurrup, Gringo, ye'll get us battered' Tony answered.

'You relax you! Mr high-and-mighty!' Gringo spat, hurt and perturbed and searching the girls' faces for some sort of validation.

'Shurrup I says!' commanded Tony, as serious as he was angry, while taking a deep draught from his pint.

Gringo was always behaving in this manner when he had cocaine on board, expressing these misguided prejudices. If it wasn't the Travellers, it was Muslims or blacks or junkies. Tony remembered the time he talked about how he would tear all hijabs off the heads of Muslim women, to which Tony asked if he would do the same to the nuns. He looked at Tony in utter bewilderment and bleated that the nuns wear their headdresses for religion; Gringo just couldn't comprehend that Muslim women wear hijabs for the same reason—religion.

And when Tony suggested that if they thought like that, then they should ban all the statues of the Virgin Mary, as she's wearing a hijab, but none of us noticed until now, Gringo lost it. He told Tony that his weird ideas weren't welcome and no-one thought they were clever either.

Tony gave Gringo a fool's pardon for all that; he knew where it came from. But, for him to start insulting Travellers in the middle of one of their people's funerals? Well, that was like playing Russian roulette with six bullets.

'Did ya pick a song?' said Tony, changing the subject as best he could.

'Yeah, Lou Reed, "Walk on the Wild Side". Ya can talk that one fairly good... and it's a bit-a *craic*, unlike fuckin' you!'

Tony considered poking fun at Gringo's coked-up homophobia, by reminding him the song is a transvestites' anthem, as he looked over his shoulder at what was going on behind.

The Travellers' funerals had always intrigued him. The men on one side standing at the bar, all dressed like they were going to interviews: shirts and slacks and shoes. Shaking hands strongly when seeing those absent from them usually; and the unspoken competition of seeing who could put the most money into the bar's cash register.

The Traveller women, all invariably sitting together, directly opposite the men. The younger ones dressed like they were on a night-out in Ibiza, and the older of the Traveller women looking very respectful and noble and proud.

In an instant, voices were raised as two Traveller men seemed to come to difference. The result being that the entire lounge stopped to look, but as quick as the argument had erupted, natural negotiators of the Traveller community were over with words of appeasement and demanding handshaking and the exchange of drinks and generally sorting out whatever was the difference.

'Yeah, they know to behave themselves in here. Only place that serves the cunts,' Gringo sneered.

Tony felt very alone at times. After he did that 'pox-of-a-multi-media course' he was never again right in himself. Studying 'signs and signifiers' in media. How these opinions/attitudes are planted. *The Decade of the Child Consumer* and how most of his generation was susceptible to trusting *anything* that was on the television because of it. Disciplinary TV then!

He often remembered the project he did, comparing and contrasting the language used when reporting two incidents of a killing. One where judges' and barristers' teenage sons had kicked to death a young man outside a nightclub in one of the most affluent parts of Dublin, with another incident of something similar from a working-class part of Dublin.

The judges' sons *all* had futures; were *top* students; *nice* boys who made a mistake!

The working-class boys were all thugs, evil, without hope of reform; they were only short of calling for the death penalty to be reinstated.

He couldn't read the newspapers after that, not even the broadsheets, as they were just as bad, but a lot more subtle. He knew there was an all-out attack on his people and on other powerless people! And no-one else seemed to see it. Tony felt at times, entirely alone.

'What songs are youse doin'?' Tony inquired of both of the girls.

'Natalie Cole, "Miss You Like Crazy"; said Josie with a bright grin

'Wow, a complicated one to take on; no bother to you, Josie!' Tony smiled. 'And Deborah?'

'Has to be Janis sweetheart! I woke up with her in me head, an' I took it as a sign.'

Just as Gringo began to speak, an all-consuming 'whist!' emerged, hushing all in The Penthouse lounge. One of the Traveller women had broken into song.

She looked to be aged about fifty years, and was dressed very elegantly with a black lace shawl around her shoulders. She had long grey-red hair, falling back. Her eyes were closed, face raised and placid as she sang a song of such weight of lamentation that Tony could feel his emotions within decidedly shift.

A song that not one of them had ever heard, yet they absorbed it in a way that told them they all knew it intimately. The song echoed down through the centuries, through its subsequent singers in their times, it carried truly through to the people with an essence that couldn't quite be described, just felt. The girls began to tear-up. The words seemed to be English or Irish, but were neither. Its tone telling all, the words did not actually matter. It ended to a chasm of impenetrable-silence, filled immediately by a rapturous thundering applause and shouts, all around.

'I hate all that diddleyie fuckin' shite!' sighed Gringo. 'What song ya doin' tonight, Tony?'

'Was thinkin' of doin', "Danny Boy"; Tony sighed back.

James (Jim) O'Brien

a former bricklayer, is a writer, journalist and blogger. He has had freelance material published in leading newspapers and magazines and is also a published short story writer.

His memoir *Against the Wind: Memoir of a Dissident Dubliner* is available in print, as an e-book and in audio format on Amazon/Audible. A keen student of Irish history, he has written and produced an audio documentary (tape/CD) on the Easter Rising.

He has lived and worked in several parts of Australia and has designed and built two homes using passive solar techniques.

Now semi-retired he lives in Victoria, Australia, with his wife Janet, where he continues to write at least a few hundred words each day.

Rebel Meg

At the end of the 'emergency' as World War Two was described in Ireland, there was a renewed effort by the Dublin Corporation to tackle slum clearances. People were moved to sprawling housing estates on the edges of the city. And so, they swapped overcrowding and squalor for more space and fresh air. But lost the strong community spirit of the old town.

After we moved to Milltown, I had lost touch with Meg Carey. Her family had chosen to move to Cabra on the north side of the city when the house they lived in was due for demolition. We had slowly drifted apart before the housing resettlement. 'Ah, sure, you have grown much too serious for me, Seán,' she said. 'All that auld Irish-Ireland stuff is not for me.'

Four years after we had all been moved away from our childhood streets, I began to attend dances, as did many of the youth of that generation. It was a very popular pastime, especially at weekends, and there were many of us that could dance extremely well. From time to time I met Meg by chance at the Four Provinces dance hall in Harcourt Street.

'Fancy seeing you here,' she said. 'I would have thought that you were more of a céilí-hopper.'

'I'm that too, Meg. But I also like modern music and even traditional jazz. So, I suppose that in your eyes that makes me a bit of an enigma.'

'Jaysus!' She rolled her eyes at my use of the last word.

On the edge of the dance floor she was usually the centre of attention amidst a group of visiting American sailors, or more often than not a group of African male medical students. She had a penchant for 'unusual men' as she would say and was quite uninhibited about the company she kept. For the mores, the times and the Ireland that we lived in, Meg disregarded the conventions and ignored the gossips.

Red hair cascading to her shoulders and with an off-the-shoulder gypsy blouse, matched with a full floating skirt, Meg would strut her stuff to the strains of 'La Cumparsita', or the *'Blue Tango'* or Pat Moran's arrangement of 'Boléro'.

'There she goes again. After a taste of the black puddin,' I suppose,' Jack Logan said with a leer as he watched her tango sensuously with a tall athletic black man. 'Jesus! Just look at her, she's welded onto him.'

'Ah, now, sure you're only jealous Jack, because she never dances like that with you,' I said.

'Get knotted Seán. I'm off for a drink at the bar. You coming?'

I declined to join him and instead stood at the edge of the dance floor and watched the dancers. As Meg passed in a perfect tango-twirl she caught my eye and mouthed 'Stay there' over her partner's shoulder. When the dance finished, she walked over to me. 'Ah! Seán, the very man I wanted to see,' she smiled. 'Take me upstairs to the bar, I want to talk to you.'

We sat at a quiet table and straight out she asked me if I knew Councillor Murphy. 'Of course, I do,' I replied. 'Is that old lecher bothering you?'

Councillor John Joe Murphy was a member of the Dublin County Council and it was rumoured that if you had an attractive wife, and if she was nice to him, he could get you advanced in the housing list queue. It was even said that if she was extra nice to him, he could get you a steady job in one of the Council departments. What was more than rumoured, and had been substantiated, was that he had impregnated the housemaid in the same month as he had his wife and that the girl had been sent to England to be 'looked after' as it was termed.

'Anyway, I have him panting for me,' Meg grinned, wickedly. 'But I need a hard man for the next stage of my plan. And I think you're the man for the job.' She leaned across the table and patted my hand, and I caught a glimpse of those full breasts that had excited me so much in our teenage games.

Murphy was a wheeler and dealer who stayed just inside the law in his business activities. My father said that he had been part of the 'black market racket' during the war years. But that he was 'well connected politically and could pass himself off as a pillar of the community.'

'Why me for heaven's sake?' I asked incredulously. But not without a hint of interest creeping into my voice.

'Because you are well known for taking a stand for a good cause. And you're not just a green flag Republican or a Holy-Joe one either, like a lot of the rest of them.'

'And you, Meg. Since when have you joined the ranks of the rebels?'

'Ah, now Seán, you know that in my own way I've always been a bit of a rebel. And you know as well as I do there are more ways than one to fight hypocrites.'

'Unconventional and extra-constitutional is the term, Meg. Or so I'm told.'

'Whatever you're having yourself, Seán. You were always one for the words. Now listen to my story.'

Two months before our meeting Meg had been standing outside the church with her brother-in-law, Pat Dolan, when Murphy had come out from the midday mass and, seeing Meg, he had made a point of saying good morning to Pat, whom he recognised as being an employee of the Council's casual labour force.

'Normally he would not have given Pat the time of day. But he stopped beside me and undressed me with his eyes.'

'Lovely wife you have there, Dolan,' he had smirked, and then passed on.

That had given Meg the idea that she could be useful in getting her sister's husband into a permanent job with the Council, if she played her cards right. She explained how in the weeks since the encounter at the church she had gone into Murphy's grocery shop and allowed him to ogle her and place his hand on her hips as he passed in and out from behind the counter. 'He can't keep his hands off me, the dirty old bastard,' she said with a grimace.

At that time in the late 1950s unemployment was at a record high throughout the country, and in Dublin a constant job, even one with low wages, kept some off the emigrant boats that left each night for England. Pat Dolan had recovered from a bout of tuberculosis some time before and was 'not fit road gang material,' as Meg put it.

'If he can get into the maintenance store out of the weather, he'll be right for life and so will Maura my sister and the five kids,' Meg explained. 'And Murphy thinks I am Pat's wife, so all I have to do is be nice to him. On certain conditions, mind you. But nobody, least of all Maura and Pat, must ever, ever, know.'

And so it was that a week later, armed with a borrowed camera and an unloaded 9mm pistol, just in case, I snuck around the back of Murphy's shop and waited outside the window until the excited Councillor Murphy took Meg into the back room. Dancing around him and flaunting her considerable charms for all she was worth, Meg had him jumping out of his trousers and pushing her onto the table within minutes. Then through the window, I took some quick shots of him in several positions, trousers around his ankles on the floor, and he trying as hard as he could to mount the teasing Meg.

Then, as agreed, up on my bike and away. We had calculated that the camera flashes would interrupt Murphy's efforts enough to allow Meg to avoid his pent-up advances. 'As a last resort, there is always this,' she said, and made an up-and-down gesture with her half-closed fist. 'The main thing is for you to get away with the photos, Seán.'

I stopped at the nearest post office and sent the roll of film to an address that Meg had given me. Mission accomplished, I returned the camera and the pistol to the quartermaster. He checked them and smiled, but he asked me no questions. We both knew it was not the sort of action that headquarters would condone.

I never saw her again. My trade took me around the country. And I never knew whether her ruse had worked or not. I was told she had gone to work in England, as many of us did then. Some years later I heard she had met up again with one of her African student boyfriends when he was an intern at a hospital in London. She had married him and gone to Kenya to live. I hoped it had worked out for them both. And I hoped she would always remain a true rebel.

End.

A piece of historical fiction, though much of the really bad history actually happened.

Seosamh Ó Cuaig

is a native Irish speaker from Cill Chiaráin in the Connemara Gaeltacht. Born into a small farmer family, he was one of the founder members of Gluaiseacht Chearta Sibhialta na Gaeltachta (The Gaeltacht Civil Rights Movement) in 1969 and has been involved in civil rights politics ever since. A former producer with Raidió na Gaeltachta, he has also worked in the print media and has translated textbooks to Irish. He was involved in the production of several television documentaries. He is now a weekly columnist with the Irish language online magazine Tuairisc.ie. Seosamh, was elected for three terms to Údarás na Gaeltachta (The Gaeltacht Authority) and for two terms to Galway County Council. Reflecting his keen interest in history and politics, he was involved in setting up the Liam and Tom O'Flaherty Society of which he is the chairperson.

Stailc Suiminte 1970

Beidh mé bródúil go deo as an gcaoi ar sheas daoine as ceantar seo Chill Chiaráin in aghaidh an fhir gnó as Uachtar Ard, Michael Keogh, a bhí ag iarraidh suimint a thabhairt i dtír le linn na stailce móire a bhí ar bun sa tír seo i 1970.

Chuaigh 750 oibrí as monarchana suiminte i Luimneach agus i nDroichead Átha ar stailc an bhliain sin ar son ardú pá. Ní nach ionadh chonaic fír ghnó deis le airgead sciobtha a dhéanamh. Bhí Michael Keogh ar dhuine acu.

Baile é Cill Chiaráin atá 70 ciliméadar siar as cathair na Gaillimhe. Tá calafort beag deas ann agus monarcha feamainne lena ais. Cuid dár saol inár n-óige ba ea a bheith ag breathnú ar na galtáin a thagadh anois agus aríst leis an min a dhéantaí den fheamainn a thabhairt go dtí an mhonarcha mhór ailgionáite a bhí i mBarcaldine in Albain.

Maidin Sathairn Cásca a bhí ann nuair a tháinig beirt fhear oibre as Cill Chiaráin chomh fada líomsa agus imní orthú go ndéanfaí dochar do chás na n-oibrithe suiminte dá gceadófaí an beart a bhí socraithe don bhaile beag an lá sin. Dúirt siad go raibh bád de mhin na feamainne luchtaithe le dhul go hAlbain nuair a tháinig Michael Keogh chomh fada leo agus gur fiafraíodh sé díobh an mbeidís sásta bád eile a bhí ag teacht isteach a fholmhú.

Bhuail amhras iad agus rinne siad fiosrúchán. Fuair siad amach gur as Glaschú a bhí sí ag teacht, gur 'Kate' an t-ainm a bhí uirthi agus gur suimint a bhí de lasta inti.

Mheas siad gur mhór an náire do mhuintir Chill Chiaráin dá ligfí an suimint i dtír.

Bhí Gluaiseacht Chearta Sibhialta na Gaeltachta bunaithe le bliain roimhe sin agus thuig siad go maith go mbeadh suim agamsa sa scéal. Bhí freisin.

Thug muid ár n-aghaidh ar chalafort Chill Chiaráin láithreach.

Níorbh fhada gur tháinig suas le scór leoraithe ar an gcéibh leis an suimint a thabhairt chun bealaigh. Tháinig fórsa láidir Gardaí Síochána freisin.

Chomh luath agus a tháinig an bád isteach agus a tosaíodh ag cur málaí suiminte aisti tharla scliúchas. Bá deacair don dream a bhí ag díluchtú aon dul chun cinn a dhéanamh.

Ní raibh ach taobhbhóthar amháin ón gcéibh go dtí an bóthar mór agus shocraigh an dream sin againne an taobhbhóthar sin a dhúnadh agus na leoraithe a stopadh dá réir. Chuaigh muid chomh fada le Mícheál Ó Cadhain as an teach tábhairne in aice láimhe agus d'iarr cead air clocha a chur as claí a gharraí trasna an bhóthair.

Thug sé an cead sin dúinn. Chuir seo Michael Keogh ar buile ar fad. Rug sé ar léine ormsa agus stróic sé go himleacán í. Bhí bean as an áit ag teacht ón siopa agus mála earraí aici. Bhuail sí anuas sa mullach leis an mála é. Chuir sin ceansú ann.

Ní dhearna na Gardaí iarracht ar bith muid a stopadh. Rud neamhghnách a bhí ansin. Is é an míniú atá agamsa air go dtí an lá atá inniu ann gurbh é an Ceannfort a bhí ar na Gardaí, Paddy Gallagher, a shábháil muid. B'as Gaeltacht Thir Chonaill é siúd agus ba mhinic roimhe sin agus ina dhiaidh sin a thug sé cothrom na Féinne do Ghluaiseacht Chearta Sibhialta na Gaeltachta. Dá mba Ceannfort ar bith eile a bheadh i gceannas an lá céanna bheadh na smachtíní amuigh ar an bpointe agus scaipeadh na mionéan curtha orainn.

Le scéal fada a dhéanamh gearr b'éigean do na leoraithe imeacht gan aon suimint iontu. D'fhan an bád ceangailte sa gcéibh.

Chuimhnigh Michael Keogh ar bheart eile ansin. Chuir sé a dhearthár a bhí ina shagart chomh fada le Éamon Ó Conghaile ag iarraidh air eadarghabháil a dhéanamh. Fear comharchumainn ba ea Éamon, fear a raibh ómós dó sa bparóiste. Oirníodh ina shagart é féin ó shin.

Bhí sé pósta le bean mhisniúil as ceantar Chill Chiaráin. Deirfiúr a bhí intí do dhuine de na fir a tháinig chugamsa ag inseacht dom faoin mbád 'Kate'. Bhí deartháir eile leí ag stopadh na suiminte freisin.

D'ith sí agus d'fheann sise an sagart a bhí tagtha chomh fada léi anois agus dúirt sí díreach amach leis gur mhór an náire an rud a bhí a dheartháir siúd, Michael Keogh, ag iarraidh a dhéanamh.

Mar sin féin fear réitigh a bhí in Éamon Ó Conghaile i gcónaí agus thoiligh sé cruinniú a ghairm idir an taobh sin againne agus an dream a bhí ag tacú le Michael Keogh. Dhéanfadh sé féin cathaoirleacht ar an gcruinniú a dúirt sé.

In Óstán Odeon i gcathair na Gaillimhe a tháinig an cruinniú le chéile. Chuaigh mé féin agus fear eile as Gluaiseacht Chearta Sibhialta na Gaeltachta,

Seán Ó Tuairisg, ann. Bhí Michael Keogh agus cúpla duine dá ghrúpa ar an taobh eile. Taobh amuigh bhí dream as Uachtar Ard ag screadach agus ag bagairt orainne.

Ní raibh na comhráití i bhfad ar bun nuair a rinne Michael Keogh bagairt ormsa. 'How would you like to be going home one night and that your mother wouldn't recognise you in the morning?' ar seisean.

'That might happen, Mr Keogh,' arsa mise, 'but would you be prepared to meet the consequences of that?'

Bhí bean as oirthear na Gaillimhe lena thaobh agus bhain an freagra sin geit aisti. 'Sign the paper they have,' ar sise.

Bhíodh corr phléascán ag tarlú i gConamara na blianta sin. Ní raibh aon bhaint ag Gluaiseacht Chearta Sibhialta na Gaeltachta leo ach chreid daoine go raibh.

Maidir leis an bpíosa páipéir a bhí i gceist is éard a bhí ansin an t-éileamh a bhí againne go gcaithfeadh an bád seoladh amach cuan Chill Chiaráin aríst ag a léithéid seo d'am gan an suimint a chur i dtír. Shínigh Michael Keogh an cháipéis gan níos mó moille.

Leis sin buaileadh an doras agus tháinig fír mhóra urrúnta isteach. Oibrithe as monarcha Irish Cement i Luimneach a bhí iontu. Dúirt siad linn gur chuala siad ar na meáin náisiúnta faoin mbeart a rinne muid i gCill Chiaráin agus ghlac siad buíochas linn. D'fhiafraigh siad dinn an raibh aon trioblóid againn anois. Dúirt muid leo nach raibh ach go raibh scata fear amuigh ag bagairt orainn.

'Fágaigí fúinne iad sin,' a dúirt siad.

D'fhág muid an chuid eile den scéal faoi na stailceoirí. Sheol an bád amach an cuan an Mháirt dar gcionn faoi mar a bhí socraithe. Ligeadh an suimint i dtír i gcalafort beag eile i dTuaisceart Chonamara ach rinneadh é sin trí shocrú speisialta a rinne na stailceoirí le Keogh. Fúthú féin a bhí sé sin ach bhí an taobh sin againne thar a bheith sásta gur éirigh linn clú an bhaile bhig a chosaint ar son chearta na n-oibrithe a bhí ar stailc.

'For the credit of the little village,' a dúirt Matt the Thresher in úrscéal Charles Kickham, *Knocknagow*. Sin é an dearcadh a bhí againne freisin.

Mar a tharla ba é Satharn Casca an lá céanna a ndeacha an stáisiún bradach raidió a bhí againn, Saor-raidió Chonamara, ar an aer i Ros Muc in aice láimhe. Go deimhin ba é scéal an bháid suiminte an chéad scéal a bhí ar an nuacht a craoladh ar an saor-raidió an tráthnóna sin.

Bhí bunú stáisiúin raidió Gaeltachta ar cheann de spriocanna a bhí ag Gluaiseacht Chearta Sibhialta na Gaeltachta nuair a bhunaigh muid an Ghluaiseacht i 1969.

I nDoire Cholm Cille dom féin an oíche tar éis Chath Thaobh an Bhogaigh chuala mé raidió bradach an cheantair sin ag craoladh—Radio Free Derry. Scríobh mé alt ar an nuachtán *Inniu* agus ceann eile ar an *Connacht*

Tribune ag rá gur cheart dúinne a leithéid de raidió a chur ar an aer i gConamara.

Níl a fhios agam ar ceann de na haltanna sin a léigh teicneoir óg cumasach i gCorcaigh, Mícheal Ó hÉalaí, nó ar duine eicínt eile a chuir ar an eolas é, ach nuair a thug sé cuairt ar Ghaillimh tamall ina dhiaidh sin chuir sé tuairisc faoin dream seo a raibh an smaoineamh faoin raidío acu.

Dúirt sé go mbeadh sé féin in ann aire a thabhairt don taobh teicniúil den scéal.

Theastaigh teach ansin le dul ag craoladh as. Bhí mise ag iarraidh é a chur i dTeach an Phiarsaigh ach ní aontódh mo chol cúigear Piaras Ó Gaora liom. Bhí aithne phearsanta ag a athair agus ag a sheanathair (mo shin-seanathairse) ar an bPiarsach agus mheas Piaras gur mhór an masla a bheadh ann briseadh isteach sa teachín.

Chuaigh an bheirt againn ar fud Ros Muc ag iarraidh teach feiliúnach a aimsiú. Bhí an margadh beagnach déanta againn faoi theach amháin nuair a bhuail amhras bean an tí go bhféadfadh sé gur dream mídhleathach eicínt a bhí fúinn a thabhairt isteach. Cheapfainn gur ar an IRA a bhí sí ag cuimhniú.

Bhuail muid isteach sa teach tábhairne, Tigh Chlarke, leis an gcéad chéim eile a bheartú. Chonaic méféin carbhán taobh amuigh den fhuinneog —carbhán a ligfí ar cios.

'Cinnte,' a dúirt Tom Clarke agus rinne muid an margadh laithreach.

Tharraing muid an carbhán chomh fada le Tigh Phiarais Uí Ghaora, rinneadh ceangal leis an gcóras leictreachais agus níorbh fhada ina dhiaidh sin go raibh muid ar an aer.

D'fhiafraigh duine de lucht na gCearta Sibhialta céard a tharlódh dá dtiocfadh na Gardaí? Cuimheoidh mé go deo ar an bhfreagra a thug Piaras Ó Gaora air. 'Scread mhaidne ort,' a dúirt sé. 'Dhóigh na Black and Tans an teach sin go talamh agus tá inmní ortsa faoi chúpla Garda suarach nach bhfuil ach dhá lá amuigh as ionad traenála an Teampaill Mhóir.'

Rinne an *Connacht Tribune* beag is fiú de scéal an Raidió. 'The Radio that could not be heard' a thug siad air. Is fíor nach raibh sé le cloisteáil i gcathair na Gaillimhe ach shroich a ghlór chomh fada le Árainn cinnte.

Fuair mé féin litir ó sheandochtúir de mhuintir Uí Bhriain a bhí ar an leaba le tinneas in Árainn nuair a chuala sé Saor-raidió Chonamara.

'Léim mé amach ar an urlár le teann bróid as,' a dúirt sé.

Bhí Jim Fahy ag obair don *Tuam Herald* ag an am. Thug sé grianghrafadóir go Ros Muc agus cuireadh an scéal ar an gcéad leathanach den nuachtán sin!

Foilsíodh grianghraf i nuachtán náisiúnta freisin. Ón gcul a tógadh é ar fhaitios go n-aithneofaí aon duine. Bhí compánach as Corcaigh, Mícheál Ó Duibhir, in éineacht le Mícheál Ó hÉalaí. Bhí sé ráite aige lena mháthair gur ag campáil go Corca Dhuibhne a bhí siad ag dul.

'Níl sé chomh héasca sin an dallamullóg a chur ormsa,' a dúirt sise i dteachtaireacht a chuir sí chuige, 'd'aithin mé an geansaí cniotáilte.'

Chaithfeadh sé gur bhuail muid an táirne ar an mullach ag an am ceart nuair a chuir muid an raidió bradach ar an aer. Tamall roimhe sin bhí cruinniú agam féin agus ag Máire Fennell le hArdstiúrthóir RTE agus lena thánaiste, John Irvine.

Cé nár thug siad aon ghealltanas b'fhacthas dúinn nach raibh siad glan in aghaidh a leithéid de stáisiún a bheith ann.

'Mura gcuirfidh sibh ar bun é cuirfidh muid féin ar bun é,' arsa mise le Hardiman.

'Cén aois thú?' ar seisean.

Bhliain agus fiche,' arsa mise.

'Tá an-mhisneach agat,' ar seisean.

Misneach nó baois na hóige?

Is deacair a rá.

Tháinig an lá ar chuma ar bith a raibh mé féin agus Tom Hardiman ar Bhord Stiúrtha Telegael. Bhí céim mhór eile tugtha chun cinn an uair sin i seirbhís chumarsáide na Gaeltachta agus na Gaeilge.

The 1970 Cement Strike

I will always be proud of the way that people of this area in Cill Chiaráin stood up against an Oughterard businessman, Michael Keogh, who was trying to land cement during the big cement strike in this country in 1970.

750 workers from cement plants in Limerick and Drogheda went on strike that year for a pay rise. Unsurprisingly, business people saw an opportunity to make a quick pound. Michael Keogh was one of them.

Cill Chiaráin is a village 70 kilometres west of Galway city. It has a beautiful little harbour and a seaweed factory beside it. When we were young, we would watch the steamers coming in now and again, taking seaweed meal to the large alginate factory in Barcaldine in Scotland.

It was Easter Saturday morning when two workmen from Cill Chiaráin approached me. They were worried that the cement workers' cause would be harmed if what was being planned for that day were allowed to go ahead.

They said that a boat of seaweed meal was loaded to go to Scotland when Michael Keogh came down to them and asked if they were willing to unload another incoming boat.

Their suspicions aroused, they made enquiries and discovered that the ship 'Kate' was coming in from Glasgow, carrying cement.

They felt it would be shameful for the people of Cill Chiaráin to let the cement ashore.

Only a year earlier, the Gaeltacht Civil Rights Movement had been set up and they knew I would be interested in the matter. And I was.

We immediately headed for Cill Chiaráin port.

It wasn't long before a score of lorries came up on the pier to take the cement away. A strong Garda Síochána force had also arrived.

As soon as the boat came in and the unloading of bags of cement began, clashes occured. The sailors found it hard to make progress.

There was only the one access road from the pier to the main road, and we decided to block it and stop the lorries. We went up to Mícheál Ó Cadhain from the nearby pub and asked his permission to move stones from his garden wall across the road.

He gave us his agreement. This infuriated Michael Keogh. He grabbed me by the shirt and tore it to my waist. Seeing this, a local woman, coming from a shop with a full shopping bag, hit him with it on the forehead. That calmed him down.

The Gardaí did nothing to stop us. That was unusual. To this day, I believe it was the Superintendent of the Gardaí, Paddy Gallagher, who saved us. He was from the Donegal Gaeltacht, and, before and after this incident, he treated the Gaeltacht Civil Rights Movement fairly. If any other Superintendent had been in charge on the same day, the truncheons would have been out on the spot and we would have been scattered.

To make a long story short, the lorries had to leave without their expected load. The boat remained tied up at the pier.

Michael Keogh thought of another move. He sent his brother, a priest, to Éamon Ó Conghaile, asking him to intervene. Éamon was in charge of the co-op and well thought of in the parish. He was himself ordained a priest later.

He was married to a courageous woman from the Cill Chiaráin area. She was the sister of the man who had told me about the boat 'Kate'. Another brother was also involved in stopping the cement.

She skinned the priest alive when he came up to her, telling him straight that what his brother, Michael Keogh, was trying to do was shameful.

Éamon Ó Conghaile, however, would always look to resolve problems, and he agreed to convene a meeting between Michael Keogh's supporters and ourselves. He himself would chair the meeting.

The meeting took place in the Odeon Hotel in Galway city. Seán Ó Tuairisg and I attended on behalf of the Gaeltacht Civil Rights Movement. Michael Keogh and a few of his group represented the other side. Outside, a group from Oughterard shouted abuse and threatened us.

The talks had hardly begun when Michael Keogh tried to intimidate me. 'How would you like to be going home one night and that your mother wouldn't recognize you in the morning?' he said menacingly in English.

'That might happen Mr Keogh,' said I, 'but would you be prepared to meet the consequences of that?'

A woman by his side, from east Galway, was taken aback by my response. 'Sign the paper they have,' she urged him.

There was the occasional explosion in Conamara back then. And while the Gaeltacht Civil Rights Movement had nothing to do with them, most people believed otherwise.

As for the piece of paper, our demand was that the boat should sail out of Cill Chiaráin harbour at a specific time without landing the cement. Michael Keogh signed the document without further delay.

With that, the door crashed open and some big, sturdy men came in. Workers from the Irish Cement factory in Limerick had arrived. They had heard in the national media about our action in Cill Chiaráin and they came to express their appreciation. They asked us if we had any trouble now. We told them a bunch of men outside were trying to intimidate us.

'Leave them to us,' they said.

We left the rest of the story to the strikers. The boat sailed out of the harbour the following Tuesday as scheduled. The cement was landed in another small port in North Conamara by special arrangement between the strikers and Keogh. We were delighted we had managed to defend the reputation of our parish in support of the rights of the striking workers.

'For the credit of the little village,' Matt the Thresher commented in Charles Kickham's novel, *Knocknagow*. That was our view too.

As it happened, that Easter Saturday was the same day our pirate radio station, Conamara Free Radio, went on air in nearby Ros Muc. In fact, the story of the cement boat was the first story on the news broadcast that evening.

The establishment of a Gaeltacht radio station had been one of the goals of the Gaeltacht Civil Rights Movement when we founded the Movement in 1969.

I was in Doire Cholm Cille (the city of Derry), the night after the Battle of the Bogside, and I heard the local pirate radio station broadcasting —Radio Free Derry. I wrote an article for the newspaper *Inniu* and another one for *The Connacht Tribune* saying that we should set up such a radio station in Conamara.

I don't know which of those articles the talented young Cork technician Mícheal Ó hÉalaí read, or if someone told him, but when he visited Galway a while later he looked for the people who had suggested a radio station.

He said he would be able to look after the technical side.

All he needed was a house to broadcast from. I wanted to use Pearse's Cottage, but my cousin Piaras Ó Gaora did not agree. His father and grandfather (my great-grandfather) had known Pearse personally and he thought it would be an insult to break into the cottage.

The two of us went all over Ros Muc trying to find a suitable house. We had almost made the deal in one house when the lady of the house became suspicious that we were part of some illegal crowd. She was probably thinking of the IRA.

We popped into the pub, Clarke's, to plan our next move. I saw a caravan outside the window—a caravan for rent.

'Sure,' Tom Clarke said and we had a deal on the spot.

We towed the caravan as far as Piaras Ó Gaora's house, connected it to the power line and soon after we were on air.

One of the Civil Rights activists asked what would happen if the Gardaí came? I will never forget Piaras Ó Gaora's response.

'To hell with you! The Black and Tans burned this house to the ground and you are worried about a few measly Gardaí who are only a couple of days out of Templemore training college.'

The Connacht Tribune made litle of the radio story. They called it 'The Radio that could not be heard'. It is true that it could not be heard in Galway city, but its voice certainly reached Aran.

I got a letter myself from an old doctor, one of the O'Brien's, who was sick in bed in Aran when he heard Conamara Free Radio.

'I leapt out on the floor with a pang of pride,' he said.

Jim Fahy was working for the Tuam Herald at the time. He took a photographer to Ros Muc and the story was featured on the front page of that newspaper!

A photo was also published in a national newspaper. The caravan was photographed from the rear for fear of being identified. A companion from Cork, Mícheal Ó Duibhir, accompanied Mícheál Ó hÉalaí. He had told his mother that they were going camping to Corca Dhuibhne.

'Don't think you can fool me,' she said in a message, 'I recognized the knitted sweater.'

We must have hit the nail on the head at the right time when the pirate radio went on air. Some time before, Máire Fennell and I had a meeting with the Director General of RTE and his deputy, John Irvine.

Although they made no promises, they did not seem to oppose the existence of such a station.

'If you don't set it up, we'll set it up ourselves,' I told Hardiman.

'What age are you?' he asked.

Twenty-one, ' I said.

'You have great courage,' he said.

Courage or the folly of youth?

It's hard to tell.

Anyway the day came that Tom Hardiman and I were on the

Telegael Board of Directors. Another leap forward in the Gaeltacht and Irish language communications service at that time.

Barbara O'Donnell

was born in West Cork in 1975, a publican's daughter. She started working in addition to school at age thirteen. She currently works full time in the NHS in London as an Operating Department Practitioner. Her poetry has been published in *Atrium Poetry, Dear Reader, Ink, Sweat & Tears, Irish Literary Society, Prole, Skylight 47, South Bank Poetry, The Night Heron Barks* and *Three Drops Press*. One of her poems was included in the Culture Matters anthology *The Children of the Nation*. 'Thresholds' is her first published essay.

Thresholds

The previous Irish State Pathologist, Professor Marie Cassidy, is on the medical talk circuit in 2019. She was Ireland's first female State Pathologist, a role which on a small island, already carries a degree of celebrity with it. A portrait of her by the Cork artist, Jack Hickey, was hung in the National Gallery of Ireland in late 2018, in recognition of her contribution to science. It's still strange to think that someone whose hands determine causes of death and give evidence in court, is someone who also touched my mother's body.

When I saw her name listed as a speaker at an Irish Medical Humanities conference, I knew she was the pathologist who carried out the post-mortem on my mother, Tui. She retired as State Pathologist two days before what would have been Tui's 84th birthday, in 2018.

Tui didn't survive the trip to hospital on a bitterly cold West Cork evening in January 2000. There was nothing left to do except get on the plane home from London the next day, heart fractured with shock and unsure of what to expect, other than a funeral. When I saw the scene in the house, complete with discarded oxygen tubing, it occurred to me that perhaps if I had been there, I might have been able to help.

But fortune dictated much earlier than these events, that in order to acquire those skills, I would have to leave the country. When I boarded the plane for London in 1994, I had no inkling that I might be asking myself a mere six years later if I could have saved my mother. Back then, I only knew that a lifetime of bartending seemed the most likely path I would wind up on. I feared the end of that path, and for a long time had no idea how I was going to change it.

Hospitals—a recurring threshold—are now the places I've spent most of my working life. When people ask about my early days in Ireland, I jokingly tell them that I just swapped one set of anaesthetic drugs for another. At times, it feels like my hospital life is a sort of fate.

Dad was in another ward at the same time as my mother was giving birth to me, kept in for intravenous antibiotics after stepping on a rusty nail. I kept my dear mum labouring with me all night and was born early in the morning.

Following my birth, Tui was admitted to a hospital in another county for her second bout of postnatal depression. Years later, when I finally found the place she had been admitted to, I applied for a copy of her medical records and received what seemed at first like a terse response. The offer they made was that I could come and sit in their office with the notes and someone present. But no photocopies or photographs could be taken at that meeting.

Though they seem far enough apart, it's hard not to emotionally connect a response like this from 'the authorities', to the newspaper stories of Magdalene women seeking their records and redress. Even as I know that there will be good reason for the tone of the response. The one childhood 'joke' that keeps echoing throughout my head is that of the 'red-brick building'. At least one of the mental hospitals in the closest big city, Cork, was made of red brick.

The 'joke' was also understood to be if you behaved like a crazy person, i.e. anything outside of the accepted norms of the time, speaking up too much, or just about any infraction at all, you could find yourself in one of these places with frightening speed. Being born female, of course, immediately put you at a disadvantage, since the 'crazy' label could be more easily made to stick.

I've spent a good deal of time wondering what happened to my mother in that place, which seemed to be most likely one of basic existence. In my worst visions, she is heavily medicated—a zombie in the white nightgown of every B movie. In Ireland, the treatment for everything is drugs—usually anti-depressants where mental health is concerned.

The threshold that I spent most of my early life in is pubs. Pubs are hospitals in and of themselves, best known for treating heartache and invisible wounds. Except there is no alternative to the oral route, and while a medical doctor may often be found on the premises, one's treatment is self-administered—with no cure found at the end of a glass.

Spending so much time living near or in states of emergency, real or imagined, means your cells constantly exist on the threshold of a fight or flight response. Anxiety becomes your keeper, determining what you may or may not achieve each day, always ensuring that you know it is in charge. Half the time, the anxiety itself resists clarification. For the other half, the reason for it is no longer valid, but you're still dealing with the fallout. The unspoken fear is that it is something else you've inherited, along with all the other things yet to be named.

In my childhood, grace and elegance were virtues to be aspired to, but never attained. Not when there were beer barrels to be changed, mixers to restock, and sticky, empty bottles to crate. If you weren't careful sorting those bottles for recycling, especially late at night, you could easily end up tearing ligaments on an errant plank and spending several weeks in plaster.

Mammy, somehow, exuded grace and elegance, possibly facilitated in a strange fashion by the rheumatoid arthritis that came on in her late thirties, and which restricted her in ways I didn't fully understand then. Or maybe it was the delicacy lent to her by being named for a bird, from New Zealand, her country of birth.

With a diagnosis of psoriatic arthritis in 2017, I am beginning to have unexpected insights into my mother's life. I remember writing a letter to a specialist in Ireland at around twelve years of age, asking what the probability was of my suffering rheumatoid arthritis later in life. While I was reassured that it normally skips a generation, what went unsaid was the possibility of developing another form of this autoimmune disease.

Because I never had the overt skin plaques some suffer, my psoriasis went undiagnosed until my forties. No doctor could ever explain why my nails were permanently ridged and my fingers like sausages, until the physician in London who diagnosed the psoriatic arthritis. Looking at a photo from twenty years ago, after dieting for a holiday, my hands remained their stubborn, swollen selves. The piano hands I craved were never going to be mine.

Marrying William E. O'Donnell, of 'Lansdowne', Cork City, was an elevation out of a life of likely poverty for Tui, who had spent most of her early years living close to the breadline. Her father left when she was twelve, leaving her mother single at a time when single mothers were always vilified and blamed. She told us stories of them packing their bags and doing 'midnight flits' because they were unable to afford the rent.

In Auckland, in 2005, I went to find the address she was born at. It was all waterfront property, with the no-doubt inflated prices to match. A long-time family friend had earlier located the last address she had lived at, before leaving to work for the New Zealand government in the Cook Islands. That building turned out to be a prefab scheduled for demolition some months earlier, but which had somehow remained standing for me to see it.

When my search of birth records and newspaper articles in the Auckland City archives uncovered further details of her father, he turned out to have died from a heart attack, aged fifty-eight, at an address around the corner from where I was staying in Mount Eden. It's a curious thing to wonder if the generations before you have already determined the method of your own passing.

Tui seems to cross thresholds over and over again to meet me. I find her in the nurse training she didn't finish and in work photographs of me that I discovered in her handbag after she died. People in my hometown would tell me she showed them the photos after they'd asked how I was. At night, she's a kind of ghost in my joints as I lie in bed, wondering if the shooting pain between my hip and knee is something she knew intimately. She's there in my afternoon nap, too, when I remember how I disturbed her sleep with endless childish questions, unaware that she was using the rest as a method of pain-relief.

Tui even made it online posthumously. In 2018, a journalist for *The Irish Examiner* contacted me to say that some photos of Mammy and Daddy in the Anchor in 1982 were going to be published in the paper. I was grateful for the warning, since it gave me a chance to brace myself emotionally for the inevitable enquiries and kind comments. Dad was just over a year passed, and much of his life is traceable in newspaper articles and even some Irish television.

The same photos suddenly reappeared again online in 2019, on a Facebook page, where the photographer is currently showcasing his work for sale. This time, there was no warning. There she is, at twenty to eleven on Christmas Eve 1982, washing glasses in a busy bar, with her lilac cardigan and glasses, the tone of the photos not quite conveying the shade of lipstick she was never seen without.

This photographer has no idea that she is dead. He is completely ignorant that every time he shows his photos off online, for interest, for clicks, that he is crossing the carefully constructed boundary of a twenty-four-year-old daughter's heart.

Lani O Hanlon

Lani's Mom, Lauri, from a working-class family, began at an early age to teach dance and study choreography, working as a performer and dance teacher, who 'tap-danced up the milk bill, the bread bill, the meat', passing this skill onto her daughters and granddaughters as a way to earn a living. Lani went on to work with holistic movement and dance to heal the trauma in her own body and then to facilitate others to do this through dance, voice and creative writing. She works in arts and health, and facilitates ecological writing retreats.

Author of *Dancing the Rainbow* (Mercier Press, 2007) and *The Little Theatre* poetry chapbook (Artlinks) Lani O Hanlon has an MA in creative writing from Lancaster University and her work has been published widely in various literary magazines and anthologies: *Poetry, Poetry Ireland Review, The Stinging Fly, The Irish Times, Mslexia, Orbis, Southword, Skylight, Abridged* and broadcast on RTE's *Sunday Miscellany.*

If You were the Only Girl

My mother was born in a tiny house at the foot of the Dublin Mountains and reared on nettles and big heads of spring cabbage that her father, Dom, grew in the plot behind the house. Later, the family moved to Rathfarnham, and our Nana Dublin's house had a little square window to the side of the door, like an eye watching, the sitting room had lots of ornaments, a piano and the figurine of a dark-haired girl with a red skirt, dancing; this, we thought, was our mother, because when she was only seven she'd won the equivalent of a man's wages, dancing and singing in the city, winning that talent competition every week until they told her she would have to stop entering.

Papa Dublin was still growing food at the very end of the back garden, and there was a swing and snapdragons that my sister Elaine and I picked and put on our fingers to make them snap. I was afraid of the bigger girls on the road, how adept they were at swinging around lampposts on a rope, their hop and kick the can across chalk squares; and Nana Dublin was busy, one daughter still at school, freshly ironed shirts hanging on the backs of doors and lunches wrapped in saved bread wrappers for her sons to bring to work the next day. When she called us into the kitchen for the treat of batch loaf, butter and jam, or a butter-cream biscuit, we'd try to look pleased but we were thinking about our other grandmother—Nana Ross, who had help in her house above a grocer's and sweet shop on Priory Street in New Ross, and when we visited her we were spoilt with ice-creams, flakes, chocolate, crisps and sweets in a paper cone, or brought over the town to Nolans or Campbells for toys, books and comics, and in summer, seaside trips to Duncannon.

At parties in Rathfarnham Nana Dublin sang 'If you were the only girl in the world...'

When she was just a little girl she was fostered and reared by two women in Tallaght, whom we were introduced to as aunts. With the self-absorption of children we didn't even question this; we didn't know that she had been fostered, who her mother was and, even now, what happened between her birth and this adoption—had she been with her mother or somewhere else? And was the lady from Howth who had visited her once a week in Tallaght, her mother? I wish that I had known about all of this because I would have immediately empathised with the fearful, lonely child she must have been, a little girl called Rosie. But Rosie had other stories, and when my mother was away we spent a whole day together cleaning out cupboards. I was fascinated by the ash on the tip of the fag in her mouth as she told me a love story about the older man with the limp who came calling, our Papa Dublin. I thought she didn't like me, but it was only that she was so busy and I didn't notice her gifts for making ends meet and her gifts of food to my mother when we were small. Later she was at every show we did, sitting in the audience enjoying it all, and there for my Debs, my wedding. I was friendly, but I held myself apart because with the heartlessness of a child I had set them up against each other—my two grandmothers, and in a way I was set up as well because I stayed with and bonded with Mary Anne, my Nana Ross when I was a baby and again for some months as a toddler when my mother was ill. When my mother finally came to collect me she told me that I turned away, rejecting her, as I thought I had been rejected.

But I'm back in Rathfarnham today, looking for Rosie's home, the one-eyed house with the snapdragons. There are no children hopping and kicking a can, though there is an echo, and I picture my mother with her dark curls bobbing, jumping rope, tap-dancing in the local hall, and how she passed on her gift for dance to my sisters and me, and our children, as a way to make a living, a way to feed ourselves.

Beyond these roles that we are all assigned: mother, daughter, sister, granddaughter, grandmother, there are women with their own inner lives and stories, and there are so many questions that I want to ask; but for most of my life I was looking the other way, away from the matrilineal line—though it lives and breathes through me, the fear of abandonment, the strong rhythm of our feet on old boards, Rosie singing at a party, the break in her voice.

Mícheál Ó hAodha

is a poet who writes in Irish. He grew up in Galway, the eldest of eleven children, and worked in the North of England for many years. His translation of Galway-born writer, Dónall Mac Amhlaigh's novel *Deoraithe* entitled *Exiles*, chronicling the working-class experience of Irish migrants to England during the 1950s will be published by Parthian, UK, in October, 2020. His chapter 'Socialist Literature in Britain: The Traces of the Irish Working Class' appeared in the volume *Marxist Perspectives on Irish Society* (Mícheál O'Flynn et al., Newcastle, UK: 2014) and his essay 'Limerick and the World: The Limerick Soviet, and the Legacy of 1919' appeared in the anthology *Let Us Rise: 1919–2019: An Anthology Commemorating the Limerick Soviet 1919*, edited by Dominic Taylor and John Liddy, Limerick: Limerick Writers' Centre Publishing (2019).

Imithe

Stopas agus sheasas ar feadh nóiméid agus na sluaite ag brostú thar bráid. D'fheacas ar ghlúin amháin amhail is dá mbeinn ag ceangal iallacha mo bhróige. Eisean a bhí ann ceart go leor. Éadan níos sleabhctha air thar mar a ba chuimhin liomsa é. A dhreach tite chun talaimh, i dtreo na hithreach. Hata olla go híseal os cionn na baithise aige. D'aithníos mar sin féin é. D'aithneoinn áit ar bith é. Bhíos i gcónaí go maith i leith aithne shúl de. Cartán folamh os a chomhair amach le haghaidh sóinseála. A chorp fillte faoina sheaicéad *bomber* borrtha. Cuma stróicthe sheanchaite ar a bhróga.

Bhí na ráflaí go léir fíor tar éis an tsaoil. Bhí sé ag cur faoi sa stáisiún traenach. Gan dídean, gan chompánach, é ag siúl an chosáin bhriste sin a dtugtar an sidewalk sa tír seo air. Ba bhacach é, traimp, *wino*, geocach, an neach úd a fágadh ar leataobh ag sruth mire an tsaoil. Tá mórán acu ann, i dtír seo na mbrionglóidí. Bhí na ráflaí fíor. Ní dheachaigh sé níos faide ná an stáisiún dó féin tar éis an tsaoil.

Tharla rud éigin aisteach dó nuair a thuirling sé ar thalamh na tíre sin cúig bliana níos luaithe. Leáigh ní dothuigthe éigin go ciúin laistigh de agus ar éigean má bhí sé in ann céim amháin a chur os comhair céim eile. Stad sé mar a raibh sé ar nós chlog an bháis a gcuirtear brat os a chionn in ómós an nua-mhairbh. Mura raibh sé feicthe agam le mo shúile féin, is ar éigean a chreidfinn mar scéal é.

Lig mé orm nach bhfaca mé é an chéad uair sin. D'fhéach mé sa treo eile. Chuireas leathlámh le mo shúile agus d'imíos as radharc go tapa isteach sa slua. Ach ní raibh mé in ann éalú uaidh, in ainneoin mo dhíchill. Gach lá agus mé ag dul isteach oscailt an subway, bhínn ag cuimhneamh air. Bhí sé ag luí ar m' intinn agus mé ag trasnú na cathrach i gcomhair mo chuid oibre; ba phrintíseach dlíodóra mé. Dreach Johnny i m'intinn i gcónaí agam. Chonaic mé é i súile na dtaistealaithe eile ar an traein faoi thalamh. Istoíche, chuireas an clog aláraim ar siúl ar imeall an chófra agus mhúchas an teilifís, shíneas

162

siar ar mo leaba *king-size* Mheiriceánach ach bhí samhail Johnny fós os mo chomhair amach. Mar scáth a bhí sé, a aghaidh i bhfolach faoina leathchaipín olla salach, na *jeans* caite, a dhroim le balla, an ghaoth fheanntach sa tollán mar chompánach aige, feic saolta eile os comhair an tslua.

Tugtha don ól agus do na *tablets*. B'in an méid a dúradh. Na mílte daoine, mo dhála féin, ag siúl thairis gach lá, iad ag ligean orthu nach bhfacadar é. Nach bhfacadar tada.

I mbun oibre san oifig teolaí smaoiníos air agus é ina shuí ansin leis féin ar feadh an lae, a chosa fillte faoi, claon-ghéagach. Ní fhéadfainn a shamhail a ruaigeadh. Eisean a bhí *do mo leanúintse* i ndáiríre. B'eisean an sealgaire agus mise mar chreach aige.

Thosaigh mé ag faire amach dó gach lá. Ag féachaint uaim. Choinníos amach uaidh amhail neach faiteach i láthair ollphéiste. Chuirfinn mo spéaclaí léitheoireachta orm dá ngabhfainn níos gaire dó. Chaitheas caipín cúpla maidin eile. Cheileas mé féin air, ar eagla na heagla. Ar éigean má d'athraigh seisean le linn na tréimhse sin. An chuma chéanna i gcónaí air, an t-ionad céanna sa tollán aige, an cartán déirce céanna agus na focail «spare change» breactha air fiú amháin. Amhail fear a bhí ag fanacht go foighneach ar ní éigin. Feitheamh fada fuar.

Trí seachtaine a thóg sé orm sa deireadh. Trí seachtaine sula raibh sé de mhisneach agam labhairt leis. Maidin fhuar a bhí ann nuair a d'fheacas síos os a chomhair. Ar ghlúin amháin a bhí mé ach thóg sé nóiméad air na súile a ardú chugam. Taobh thiar díom, bhraitheas súile na gcéadta ag dó tríom, mo dhroim ar lasadh leis na céadta, ní hea, na mílte súil. "Ná habair nach n-aithníonn tú mé, a f*****!'

D'fhéach sé ar orm ar feadh cúpla soicind agus chonaic mé ansin sna súile aige é, chomh soiléir leis an lá. Na slabhraí dofheicthe a bhí teannta timpeall air. Chuir mé amach mo lámh ach d'éirigh sé ar a chosa dá dheoin féin. Cheannaíos caife don bheirt againn agus shuíomar le chéile ar bhinse —gróigthe ansin le chéile os comhair an chláir ama ollmhóir a bhí ag preabarnach mar a bheadh súil mhór an domhain ann.

Ní cuimhin liom mórán den chomhrá a bhí againn an chéad lá sin. Comhrá gearr a bhí ann, is cinnte sin. Bhog sé go corrthónach ar an mbinse. Bhogas-sa leis. Amhail ceoltóirí i mbun fonn bodhar an mhí-shuaimhnis a bhíomar beirt. Tháinig beocht éigin sna súile aige nuair a shlog sé siar an caife scallta, áfach. Níor thagair mé don am atá caite go dtí an tríú huair ar bhuaileamar le chéile nuair a roinneamar mála taoschnónna.

Bhí a shúile mar an gcéanna. Gorm céanna an athar agus a sheanathar roimhe. A éadan a bhí tar éis athrú. Dreach claiseach caite amhail fear a raibh a shaol caite ag obair faoin aer aige. Garraí na gcloch briste. Bhíos ábhairín déanach ag dul ag obair an lá sin. D'imíomar beirt siar ar bhóithrín na smaointe. Ar dhíon an gharáiste sa sean-eastát tithíochta fadó a bhíomar arís.

Ag spraoi mar is dual do pháistí. Ag gáirí go mailíseach agus an clampar ar siúl i dtigh Mhic Conaill thíos fúinn. Na páistí agus na tuismitheoirí ag tabhairt léasadh béil dá chéile maidin is oíche. Faoi dheireadh, an mháthair, Sally, ag rith amach an príomhdhoras, cás taistil folamh ina lámh aici. A fear céile agus an mac is sine á gcáineadh aici i nguth láidir na seanfhilí, í ag caitheamh an cháis taistil thar an mballa. 'Imigí libh mar sin, a amadána,' ar sí de bhéic. 'Agus fán fada oraibh!

Sally M., a mbíodh an fhallaing sheomra á caitheamh ar feadh an lae go minic aici, an toitín leathlasta ar chúinne a béil aici. Bean dhorcha dhathúil, duine teasaí arbh fhiú troid ar a son! Ba leabhar oscailte é an saol an uair úd, ballaí na dtithe chomh tanaí le páipéar bhosca na Nollag. Ní raibh éinne ina oileán ná ina oileánach. Níor theastaigh ó éinne a bheith difriúil ná scoite amach ón gcuid eile. Ba chuid den rud eile sin é sinne, pé rud é, má ba bhriste féin é is gan ainm. Mé féin is Johnny thart ar an imeall ar feadh scaithimh.

Níor thug mé airgead dó agus níor iarr sé riamh orm é. Níor luamar an saol mar a bhí anois, ná an stáisiún traenach ba bhaile anois aige. Cé mar a chaith sé an saol le blianta beaga anuas. B'in an t-aon slí a bhí fágtha agam, a shaol a shamhlú. Lá éigin, an lá ar ghéill sé sa deireadh agus radharc aige ar an gcríoch, ba dhóigh leat, agus cruth eile anois ar an am. Rinne mé iarracht saol laethúil Johnny a shamhlú, mé féin a shamhlú sa riocht céanna leis. Na francaigh agus an torann gan staonadh, an foréigean fíochmhar faoi thalamh, tafann síoraí na ndaoine gortaithe thart timpeall air. Tháinig na híomhánna ar nós macallaí ráillí iarnróid fadtréigthe. An traein ag teacht chun ceann scríbe. Is cuma le gach éinne... *Is cuma... Ní thabharfaidh éinne tada faoi deara. Tá mo néaróga briste brúite. Lá amháin agus ansin, an chéad lá eile. Ní féidir liom. Níl puinn fuinnimh fágtha ionam. Faoi dheireadh...*

Clog mór an stáisiún traenach ag ainliú os ár gcionn an lá ar thugas cuireadh dó teacht chun an tí. 'Tá jab agam dúinn beirt. Adhmad, a mhac. Adhmad.'

Déardaoin. An t-adhmad carntha sa chlós agam. Sean-chrainn. Boladh na beatha agus boladh an bháis measctha le chéile. Boladh idir eatarthu an tsaoil. Bruithniú an roisín agus na mbrainsí stróicthe. Na fréamhacha ar tarraingíodh ón ithir iad. Déanann siad carn ollmhór gránna i mbun an ghairdín, i gcoinne an bhalla mar a scaoil an trucail isteach iad. Tógann Johnny an sábh slabhrach ina lámh, gan focal. Caitheann sé a sheaicéad ar leataobh ar an bhféar. Tá sé níos tanaí ná mar a shíl mé. Filleann sé siar muinchillí a léine. Fágtar mise leis an tua. Tarraingíonn sé an *choke* agus *away* linn. Ionsaíonn sé an carn adhmaid. Oibríonn sé go tapa, é ag gearradh an adhmaid ina bpíosaí agus ina bpíosaí, é ag cur a riocht féin orthu. Agus mise?

Níl mórán eolais agamsa i dtaobh na hoibre seo. Seans gur mó de bhac atá ionam i ndáiríre. Tá Johnny i lár baill agus mise á chiorclú ar imeall an chairn, mé ag iarraidh an t-adhmad a bhfuil maitheas ann a scaradh ón dríodar. Na lomáin lofa sin atá lán de thaise agus nach féidir a úsáid. An tua im ghlac agam, níl ionam i ndáiríre ach breathnóir. Is é Johnny an buachaill chuige, é ag luascadh isteach is amach ar nós dornálaí, matáin a ghéag go teann. Fear troda i mbun catha. Baineann sé pléisiúr as. Is féidir liom sásamh a choirp a bhrath ainneoin ghlamanna an tsáibh. Cuar a cholainne, é ag druidim i dtreo an adhmaid, chomh gar sin dó nach gceadófaí sciorradh. Na rudaí is lú sa saol seo is mó a thugann sásamh. Cruth eile ar an am anois.

Ní hé seo an oifig ná an tsráid. Níl tábhacht dá laghad leis na gnéithe saoil sin anois mar tá jab eile ar láimh againn anseo, dúshlán atá le cur dínn, gan mhoill. Agus tá an gearradh seo ar siúl tráthnóna Fómhair ar ithir Mheiriceá. Tá an lá éirithe i bhfad níos fuaire. Tá an spéir gorm dorcha agus tá an ghaoth míshuaimhneach sna crainn feadh na hascaille.

Tá mo dhroim tinn ó bheith cromtha os cionn an adhmaid, an tua i mo lámh agam. Righním mo chorp agus seasaim, leathlámh le mo dhroim. 'A Íosa Críost, cosúil le sean-leaideanna atáimid,' a deirimse le Johnny, ag síneadh an bhosca toitíní ina threo. Pé rud a thit amach anseo um thráthnóna, ní mar a shamhlaigh mé atá sé, áfach. Cibé rud a bhí mé ag súil leis, tá sé imithe i léig ar shlí aisteach dothuigthe éigin. Is mór idir an t-am atá thart agus an lá inniu. Tá constaic eadrainn. Ní deartháireacha a thuilleadh muid.

Ar nós leanaí ag caitheamh clocha i loch uisce atáimid le fírinne.

D'fhéadfadh an bheirt againn seasamh ar bhruach an locha sin go deo na ndeor. Tá an leoithne ghaoithe ag dul i dtreise, an t-aer ag dul i bhfuaire, an domhan ag éirí corrach. An smaoineamh a bhí agam—go n-iarrfainn air fanacht thar oíche, a ghéaga a shíneadh ar leaba chompordach agus dreas deas codlata a bheith aige, caife a ól liom an mhaidin dár gcionn—níl bun ná barr anois leis. Amhail is gur duine éigin eile é.

Fiú anois, agus an bheirt againn ag caitheamh tobac go ciúin i bhfochair a chéile, ár n-anáil ag ardú os ár gcionn ar an aer tais, tuigim go bhfuil a chuid smaointe siúd in áit éigin eile. Ag smaoineamh cheana féin ar dhul ar ais chun an stáisiúin traenach atá sé, ionad luí a lorg i gcomhair na hoíche. Airím go maith é. *Imithe* atá sé. Cheana féin. Imithe. Leanaim a shúile go fíor na spéire, ribín gorm stróicthe fhíor na spéire. An gorm. Imithe. Imithe i léig.

Gone

I stopped and stood still as the crowds hurried past, then went down on one knee as if to tie my laces. It was him alright. His face was longer than I remembered it, as if it had drooped. He wore a woolly hat pulled low over his forehead but I knew him. I was always good on faces. He held an empty carton in front of him, his body wrapped in a big bomber jacket. His boots were broken and scuffed. So the rumours were true after all. He was living in the train station. He was living rough in the cold wind, and walking the broken path they called the sidewalk in this country. He was a beggar, a tramp, a wino, an acid freak, whatever they called them in this place. And they were everywhere here, in the 'land of plenty'.

The rumours were true, after all. He hadn't got beyond the station when he'd arrived five years ago, or whatever it was. Something had happened. Something had melted quietly inside of him and he had been unable to walk another step. He had stopped just like that, right where he was, like a clock draped for the new-dead. If I hadn't seen it with my own eyes, I wouldn't have believed.

I ignored him that first day, looked the other way, and raised a hand to my face as I walked by and melted into the crowd. But I couldn't get him out of my head. Every day that I went into the subway to cross the city for work— I was working as a trainee lawyer then—I couldn't get Johnny out of my head. At night, when I set the alarm clock and switched off the TV and lay myself down in that kingsize American bed, I couldn't get the image of him out of my mind. His face half-hidden beneath that dirty-looking woollen cap, the faded jeans, his resigned posture, back to the wall, facing the crowds. He was addicted to drink and different types of drugs. Some kind of tabs is what the lads said at home. That's what they had said. The thousands of people, like me who ran by him each day and pretended not to see him. I thought of him sitting there all day, cross-legged in the knife-like cold that whipped along the tunnels and corridors of that train station, that big monster's mouth of the morning. I began to look out for him each day.

I watched him from a distance. Sometimes I put my glasses on to disguise myself. And when I got closer. Just in case. His position rarely changed. Always the same, the carton and the cardboard sign on which the words 'spare change' were scrawled. It took me three weeks before I mustered the courage to talk to him. It was a freezing cold morning when I went down on one knee.

'You don't recognise me, you f...r.'

He looked at me for a moment and I saw it there in his eyes, as clear as day. All the invisible chains that were wrapped around him. I put out my hand but he helped himself to his feet. Then bought some coffee. We sat together on one of the benches opposite the giant timetable that flickered above us, like the great eye of the world. I can't remember much now about that first conversation. It was a short one. He shifted uncomfortably in his seat, but I saw some life come into him when he drank the scalding coffee. I didn't bring up the past until the third time we met, when we shared a bag of doughnuts.

His eyes were the same. The same blue as his father and his grandfather. It was the face that had changed. Furrowed and worn. A field of broken stones. Like he, too, belonged to the past.

The back-roof where we used to play as kids and the roaring that went on, morning and night in McConnells, the kids and the parents berating each other. Stella M. and how she regularly threw her eldest sons and her husband out of the house in a symbolic act—flinging the empty suitcase across the broken country driveway. 'Off with ye and don't bloody come back! You fools!' Stella, who wore the dressing gown half the day, and who always had the fag hanging at the corner of her lips. A woman worth fighting for! Our lives were an open book back then, the walls of the houses so thin. No-one was cut loose because it just wasn't possible. It was different in those days because nobody wanted to remain aloof. There was no honour in remaining aloof. We all felt part of something, even if it was unnamed and broken. I never gave him money and I never asked him about what had happened to him in previous years. We skirted around the edges for a few weeks, Johnny and I. This was the only way. I imagined myself into his world. One day—the day when he gave up—as if the end was in sight and where time assumed a different nature for him. The rats and the noise and the vicious violence and the baying of hurt people all around him. All the phrases like the echoes of a railtrack and the train coming towards journey's end. *Who cares? It doesn't matter. No-one will notice. My nerves are shot. One day at a time. I can't even if I try ... I come the end...'* The giant clock hovered above us the day I asked him to come over. I've got a job for us. *Timber.*

Thursday. The wood is piled in the yard. The smell of resin and torn trees. Branches torn from the earth. It forms an ugly pile against the back wall where the truck let it fall. Johnny doesn't say a word. He takes the chainsaw in hand, throws off his jacket on the grass, rolls up his sleeves. He is thinner than I remember. He pulls the 'choke' and away we go. He works quickly and the fresh wood falls into even lengths. He makes them his own.

And as for me? I know little about this sort of work. I'm more of a hindrance than a help. Johnny's in the centre and I'm skirting the edges, sifting away what is damp or useless. Axe in hand, I am really only a spectator. He circles and weaves like a boxer, his muscles taut. It is a battle and he loves it. I can sense the pleasure in his body despite the deafening howl of the saw. His body forms an arc and then he pulls himself close to the timber, so close that there is no room for slippage, no room for error. Time assumes a different shape. It is the small things in life that give the greatest satisfaction.

This is not the office or the street. These things are no longer important now because there is a job in hand, a job that has to be done here and now, a job cutting timber on an autumn evening, a job that can no longer be put off. By the time we are finished with the wood it has become much colder. The sky is a dark blue, and the wind is stirring in the trees along the avenue. I am stiff from the work, and when I stand upright I place my hand against my back. 'Jesus, we're like old men,' I say as I hand John a cigarette. It's not like old times, however. Whatever I was hoping for from this strange encounter has faded away.

Something immense lies between us, as a great expanse of water. We are no longer brothers. We are just as children, throwing stones into the lake back west. We could stand at the edge of that forgotten lake forever. The air is cold and restless. Stay the night, sleep in a warm bed, drink coffee with me in the morning—it seems as nothing now. Even now as we stand smoking quietly, our breaths mingling on the air, I can tell that he is already thinking of where he will bed down for the night. He is gone already, his mind elsewhere. I follow his eyes to the horizon where the last blue ribbon of the day is already fading.

Eoin Ó Murchú

is a leftwing journalist who played a leading role in the Irish communist movement in the eighties and nineties, and before that in the Irish Republican movement in the sixties and seventies.

He was born and brought up in London, in a strongly Irish household. His people, including cousins, aunts, uncles and grandparents were all part of the Irish diaspora.

His father's family had been evicted during the Great Famine of the 1840s and driven, starving, destitute and psychologically devastated to England. They never forgot the land of their ancestry, and combined their experience of normal working-class life in post-war London with their strong antipathy to the English colonisation of Ireland.

This short memory might throw some contemporary light on why so many young Moslems and South Asians are totally alienated from the English society in which they live.

Cuimhní

Is ar éigin a gcreideann mo ghar-clann mé nuair a deirim ní hamháin nach raibh i-padanna nó idirlíon againn agus mé imo pháiste, ach ní raibh telefís sa teach go raibh aois a haondéag sroichte agam.

Ní féidir leó a leitheid de shaol seasc a shamhailt.

Ach ní raibh sé seasc ar chor ar bith: bhí ceól aghainn, cómhrá, díospóireacht faoi pholaitíocht agus faoin stair. Stair ár sinsear thar aon rud: cén chaoi gur tháinig muid go Sasana mar oileán sibhialtacht i lár mhuir na namhad?

Sea, má bhí ciníochas frith-Éireannach ag ár naimhde ní raibh mórán measa againne orthu ach an oiread. Barbarthaigh gan dabht, mar cé eile a chuirfeadh sibhialtacht faoi chois a bhí chómh saibhir sin i dteanga, i gceól, i scéalaíocht, agus i léinn.

Mar sin, nuair a dúradh linn 'go back to where you come from', bhí gliondar orainn mar bhíothas ag tabhairt aitheantas don fhíric nár bhain muid leis an tír sin, ach gur bhain muid le háit éicínt eile agus bhain áit éicínt eile linn.

Bhí an ceól agus an amhránaíocht againn sa mbaile, agus an tuiscint ar an stair: an ghráin do choras na dtiarnaí talún is lucht na dúshaothraithe ar gach leibhéal, ina measc an boss/Sir a cuireadh a scáth orainne páistí mar fholáireamh i gcoinne droch-iompar. 'Gheobhaidh Sir thú!'

Bhí gráin ag mo mhuintir don Sir sin, íomhá an oilc gan dabht.

Sea, bhí ár sibhialtacht féin nach mor againn, ach an teanga? Ní raibh ach cúpla focal is cúpla abairtí ag mo thuismitheóirí, agus iad fuaimnithe go mícheart go minic. Rud eile a goideadh uainn: ár nduchas, ár dtalamh, ár saíocht, ár dínit, agus ár dteanga.

Ar ndóigh, déanach san oíche bhí muid in ann Radio Éireann a fháil, ach ceól níos mó ná teanga a bhí le clos—agus ba ar éigin.

Bhí mé fós óg nuair a chuala mé go fírinneach an Ghaeilge dhá labhairt an chéad uair. Chuaigh duine demo chuid deartháireacha suas go Londain (bhí cónaí orainn ar imeall na cathrach móire sin) is thainig sé abhaile le cúrsa Linguaphone.

Bhí sé in ann íoc as toisc go raibh jaibín páirtaimseartha aige, cé go raibh air cuid mhaith dá pháigh a thabhairt don teaghlach (rud eile nach dtuigeann mo ghar-chlann).

Ar aon chuma, bhailigh muid i gciorcal timpeall an seinnteóir cheirnín, díreach mar a bhalaíodh muid le héisteacht leis an raidió.

Is ansin a chuala mé í, agus is cuimhin liom fós na focla draíochta sin: 'Tá duine, beirt, tríúr, ceathrar, cúigear, seisear, mórsheisear sa lion tí. Sin é an t-athair, an mháthair, an sean-athair, an tsean-mháthair, an mac, an iníon agus an naíonán.'

Thiontaigh m'athair orm, agus go sollúnta d'inis sé dom gurb í seo mo theanga dúchais féin. Teanga a bhain liomsa, agus lemo mhuintir, is nár bhain leó siúd a chaith sa deóraíocht agus sa mbochtanas muid, agus a choinnigh muid ann.

Sea, bhí muid buailte ag gabháil na nGall ar ár dtír dhúchais, tír nach bhfaca muid go dtí gur tháinig rud beag airgid isteach sa teach nuair a d'imigh oidhreacht an chogaidh is gur cuireadh deire le ciondáil.

Chinn mé ansin, agus mé aistrithe ag draíocht na fuaime, go nglacfainn seilbh ar an teanga sin, go gcuirfinn gabháil na nGall orainn ar ceal chómh fada is a bhain liom féin.

Saoirse. Saoirse ó éagóir an tsaoil rachmasaigh, ó éagóir na staire, ó ghéilleadh do riail na n-uasal mar a chonacthas do James Connolly é, ceannaire na n-oibrithe i 1916. Agus Saoirse ó thoradh na gabhála is an díshealbhaithe, saoirse lenár gcultúr is ár dteanga a fháil ar ais.

Ní raibh sé éasca ar ndóigh, mar ní raibh ach na cúpla focail ag m'athair is ag mo mháthair, is ni raibh aon airgead sa teach le híoc as ceachtanna foirmeálta. Go deimhin, is cuimhin liom an stailc fhada a rinne na fir bhus (ag an am ní dóigh liom go raibh aon mhná bhus ann) faoi cheannas Frank Cousins, an ceannaire clúiteach ar an gceardchumann an TGWU (Unite mar atá anois) bliain nó dó i ndiaidh gur chuala mé an teanga.

Níor thuig mé mórán dá raibh ar siúl, ach spreag sé cuimhne eile ionam ó bhí mé fíor-óg.

Theastaigh uaim, agus mé cheithre bhliain d'aois nó mar sin, go bhfanfadh m'athair sa mbaile liom ag súgradh (sealoibrí ar ndóigh ar na busanna ab ea é). Ach duirt sé nach ligfeadh Sir dó é sin. Ná bac le Sir, dúirt mé. Ó, caithfidh mé, dúirt sé, nó ní ligfeadh Sir dúinn aon bhia a bheith againn faoi mar nár lig na tiarnaí talún dár sinsir, is go mbeadh ocras orainn.

Bhí mé ar buile. Is gheall mé dom athair, nuair a bheinn fásta go dtabharfainn poc sa ghob do Sir.

Rinne sé gáire, ach go fírinneach tá mé ag iarraidh an poc sin a thabhairt do Sir ó shoin, is tá go fóill. Agus cuid den iarracht sin is ea athghabháil mo theanga dúchais.

Memory

My grandchildren hardly believe me when I tell them that not only did we not have iPads or Internet when I was a child, but we didn't even have a television until I was about eleven.

They can't imagine such a barren life.

But it wasn't actually barren at all; we had music, conversation, debates about politics and history. The history of our ancestors above all— how come that we landed up in England, an island of civilisation in a sea of enemies?

Yes, if our enemies were anti-Irish racists, we didn't have much respect for them either. Barbarians, without a doubt, for who else would suppress a civilisation that was so rich in language, in music, in storytelling and in learning?

So when they told us to 'go back to where you come from', we were delighted because it was an acknowledgement that we didn't belong there, but belonged somewhere else, and that somewhere else belonged to us.

We had the music and the singing at home, and our knowledge of history—hatred for the landlord system and for exploiters at all levels, among them the boss, Sir, whose shadow was thrown up to us as a warning against bad behaviour. 'Sir will get you!'

My family hated Sir, an image of evil without doubt.

Yes, we had our own civilisation, more or less, but the language? My parents only had a few words or phrases, often wrongly pronounced. Another thing which had been stolen from us: our native things, our land, our wisdom, our dignity, and our language.

Of course, late at night we could hear Radio Éireann, but it was music more than language that we heard—and that barely.

I was still young when I really heard the Irish language being spoken for the first time. One of my brothers had gone up to London (we lived on the edge of that great city) and he came home with a Linguaphone course.

He was able to buy it as he had a part-time job, although he had to give up a big chunk of it to the family (something else my grandchildren don't understand).

Anyway, we gathered in a circle around the record player, just like we did to listen to the radio.

And then I heard it, and I can still recall those magic words: Tá duine, beirt, tríúr, ceathrar, cúigear, seisear, mórsheisear sa lion tí. Sin é an t-athair, an mháthair, an sean-athair, an tsean-mháthair, an mac, an iníon agus an naíonán. (There are one, two, three, four, five, six, seven people in the family. That is the father, the mother, the grandfather, the grandmother, the son, the daughter, and the infant).

My father turned to me, and solemnly told me that this was my native language—a language that had been taken from me and from my people, a language that had nothing to do with those who had evicted us into exile and poverty during the Great Famine, and who kept us there.

Yes, we had been beaten by the English conquest of our native land, a land which we never saw until a bit of money came into the house when the aftermath of the war was gone and rationing was ended.

I decided then, transported by the magic of the sounds, that I would take that language back, that I would cancel out that aspect of the foreign conquest so far as it affected me.

Freedom. Freedom from the injustice of the capitalist way of life, from the injustice of history, from our surrender to the rule of the toffs as James Connolly, the workers' leader in 1916, had seen. And freedom from the result of the conquest, the evictions, our culture and our language.

It wasn't easy, of course, for my father and mother only had a few words, and there was no money in the house to pay for private tuition. Indeed, I remember the big strike when the busmen (at the time I don't recall there being any buswomen) went out under the leadership of Frank Cousins, the legendary leader of the TGWU trades union (Unite it is called now) a year or two after I first heard the language.

I didn't understand much of what was going on, but it brought back to memory something else from when I was very young.

When I was about four years old or so, I wanted my father to stay home playing with me (he was a shift worker on the buses). But he said that Sir wouldn't let him. Don't mind Sir, I said. Oh, I must he replied or else Sir wouldn't let us have any food, just like the landlords had with our ancestors, and we would be hungry.

I was furious. I promised my father that when I grew up I would punch Sir on the nose.

He laughed, but really I've been trying to give Sir that punch ever since, and still am. And part of that effort is taking back my native language.

Karl Parkinson

is a writer from Dublin. He has lived in the inner-city council flats of Dublin for forty years. He is the author of three poetry collections and a novel, *The Blocks* (New Binary Press, 2016). His latest work, *Sacred Symphony*, is published by Culture Matters.

Before becoming a writer and creative writing teacher, he worked on building sites, in factories, as a stagehand, and as an industrial cleaner.

Deano And The Boys From The Block: Word portrait of an inner city youth

The green, stoned, mad eyes of Dean Baker looked up and down the street; he spat phlegm, almost hitting an old woman walking with her shopping trolley dragging behind. When she harrumphed he sniggered and took a long, loud drag on a joint, then blew smoke out his hyena mouth. Smiled, looked back at the street, spat again. Deano occupied the street most days of the week, the boys and him sold cannabis, coke, crack and heroin.

Dean watched his patch, watched his cohorts, watched out for Garda, watched out for rats, watched for customers, watched the girls go by, watched for trouble, watched the street.

Two skinny junkies walked on to the street; one had a light grey tracksuit on with the hood pulled up, the other was wearing a green Nike bubble jacket that was too big for him, and black tracksuit bottoms with unknowable stains on them. Grey tracksuit walked ahead, his eyes darting about the street, his neck and head bobbing like a strung out pigeon. Bubble jacket walked painfully slowly behind, scratching his inner thigh, the back of his head, his face; he spoke words to himself, his friend, to nobody in particular, mumbling interminable incantations to the wind. Dean spotted the pair, and seen cash-money walking into his domain. He whistled. Grey tracksuit looked up. Green coat's head slllooooowwwwwllllllllyyyyyyyy turned side to side. He squeaked out the words:

Where's tha?

Over der, Deano's out, said grey tracksuit.

Ah, lovely.

Dean sprinted and met the twosome.

What yiz looking for, heads?

Four bags a white, and two brown.

Four white, two brown, sound.

Dean let out a call, and an obese teenage youngfella named Chunk came out from a garden of a house across the street, looked over at Dean and nodded. A slim boy with a face like a rodent crossed with a man, whose name was Rizzer. He seemed to emerge from a crack in the ground and stood a few feet away against the wall of the corner of the street's entrance.

Deano said four to Rizzer, and held up two fingers to Chunk.

Right, they'll sorts yiz out lads.

The junkies walked over to Rizzer, and grey tracksuit handed the cash for the drugs. Rizzer took the money for all six bags, handed over four small bags of wrapped heroin, and said:

Go over to him, and he'll give yiz de bags of white, yeah.

Grand, nice one pal, said grey tracksuit.

The junkies walked over to Chunk, and he handed the two bags to them. Deal done.

Dean watched; business was all good. He took out his phone and put on a video of a Versatile song, bopped his head to the tune, toked on his joint and went back to watching the street. He'd wait half an hour then head down to the Glimmerman to meet his older cousin Robbie for a pint, and to talk business.

The lads would keep the shop open while he was away. He took another drag of the joint, hocked, spat, whistled at the next customer...

II

Dean took two quick pulls, blew smoke out his nostrils, handed the joint to Horsehead, then punched Horsehead in the stomach just as he was taking a drag of the joint. Horse coughed and spluttered, and exhaled a burst of smoke. Tricky, Chunk, and Rizzer all broke into laughter.

Yuh fuckin prick yuh Deano, said Horse, still coughing a bit, his eyes watery and red.

Ah shut up, Horse, I'm only buzzing off yuh.

Horsehead spat a greenish blob of phlegm onto the ground, laughed and said, let me take this drag properly and don't mess yuh fuckin sap. He took a big pull on the joint, blew smoke into Dean's face, then handed the joint to Chunk.

Chunk went and sat on the path, lowering his large frame to the ground, avoiding Horse's spit. He smoked the joint slowly, relishing the pulls he took on it, letting hardly any smoke out on exhalations. Fuckin swallow the smoke, look at that boys, hardly anything comes out of him, said Rizzer, stood there topless, a tattoo of his dead brother's face on his chest. It looked like Robert De Niro and it looked like his dead brother too, or like his dead brother was being played by De Niro in a movie. He had a number of other tats as well, random shit, a spiral on his shoulder, a dog's head with a dagger stuck in it on his left forearm, a naked woman with a pistol between her legs was on his right forearm, and across his belly the words *Made in Dublin*, with stars on each end of the script for no apparent reason. Chunk handed the joint to Rizzer, and Riz took it between his finger and thumb, and held it like a big cigar, even though it was the butt end of the spliff. He made a big show of taking drags, noisily sucking, and then extending his arm out and waving the butt, and then hoofing the butt down to the roach at the end, burning his fingertips a little, then he dropped the butt to the ground and stood it out. Dean watched him and said:

Jesus, Rizzer, yuh swear yuh were smoking a big cone the way yer going on there hah.

That's how I smoke all me joints Deano, yuh know me pal.

We all know, that's the problem, said Chunk from below.

Shut up you, you're lucky we let your fat arse know any of us.

Laughter, smirks.

I'm so blessed to know yiz lads, I really am.

Dean spotted a regular customer approaching, gave a nod to Tricky and said:

Here, Trick, get this one, yeah.

Tricky turned his head towards the junkie.

No way is this cunt for real, strolling in here like he's coola boola, when he owes me 40 euro for tick I gave him.

Horsehead kicked an empty can into the road, and said:

Why did yuh give him fuckin tick for?

Cause he's always in isin he, but it's about three weeks since I saw him.

Chunk stood up and stretched his arms out, and said:

Well he better have the 40 quid, so, or he's getting nothing else, yeah?

Fuckin course he better, or he's getting something all right, just not what he wants, a few digs is what he's getting.

The junkie, tall, skinny as a bird's leg, wearing a pink T-shirt and green bottoms, with a five day beard, missing a front tooth, sweat dripping down from his greasy black hair, walked right up to the boys.

Alright, lads, have yiz anything there? I'm looking for two bags.

Tricky stepped out in front of the man and said:

Have yuh got that 40 blips that yuh owe?

Wha? I don't owe any 40 bleeding blips to anyone.

Here, pal, don't try and play the fool, yuh owe me, from about three weeks ago, for tick I gave yuh.

The boys surrounded the junkie; he shook his head, claiming no knowledge of getting tick, pleading.

Dean kicked him in the side, and chunk slapped the man hard in the face, then Rizzer lunged forward and punched the junkie, busting his nose, and knocking the man over. As he fell Tricky kicked him in the chest; the man was sprawled out on his back, and the boys stomped on him repeatedly as he hollered and groaned, till he went unconscious, bleeding, on the ground. The boys went back and stood and sat at the wall, and Rizzer rolled a joint.

The junkie came around, dusted and wiped himself down, and wobbled out of the street as children on bikes chased him and threw coins and stones at him. The Boys laughed, and smoked, and took the piss out of each other.

III

The coca leaf swayed on the bush.
Split from the coca Familia.
Ripped and thrown down.
Scraped from the hands of a poor farmer in Columbia.
Began a journey to the nose of Dean Baker.
Transmogrified in a chemical metamorphosis.
From green to white, under the farmer's feet.
Out in the jungle the dark alchemy performed.
Plant to Saturday night brain rot-shite.
Black bags, gun shots and dead bodies in its wake.
Wrapped in a block for shipment to Europe, Amsterdam, Dublin.
It took up with Death. Commodity of man. Candyfloss for the brain.
Magic demonic dust. It became bills, and pounds, and euro notes.
Its name was no longer coca, but sniff, banger, snow, bread, white, nose candy, Charlie, blow, coke.
It was in a small plastic bag. A line on a CD cover.
A line moving through a paper tunnel leading to Dean Baker's nose.
It was dark in there and it moved through it.
Its name was high. It rushed through to somewhere full of lights.
It was neurons, it was in the bloodstream, nervous system, it was gone, like a boom, crack, a tat-tat, just like that, yeah, just like that, it was gone.

Ticket to ride, white line highway
Tell all your friends, they can go my way
Pay your toll, sell your soul
Pound for pound costs more than gold
The longer you stay, the more you pay
My white lines go a long way
Either up your nose or through your vein
With nothin' to gain except killin' your brain
higher, baby
(Ahh) get higher, baby
(Ahh) get higher, baby

176

And don't ever come down! (Freebase!)

Dean Baker, wiry and wild, eyes like a hyena, blade in his pocket, freshly bought white Adidas runners, a black Reebok tracksuit with a hood. He smoked joints, bongs, pipes, five skinners, ten skinners, cocaine on tap, biggest bags in Dublin, nicest sniff in the land, had the best brown in town. He was up all night all the time, a few zimmos for the come down, he loved to *ride a bird at a party, tell her she's fucking lovely, cum on her face, lovely*. Dean Baker, young terror in the city, criminal mind in overdrive, scourge of society, nihilistic, modern outlaw, Billy the Kid in the council flats, gunslinger in the gaff party, Deano, Deany, Deanzer, mad Dean, Bad Dean, Don Deano, The Dean, mean Dean, crazy Dean, doesn't give a rat's about nuttin, Dean.

Dean and three of his boys were drunk and high, two boxes of bottles had been downed, a half ounce of coke hoofed up their noses. They shoved each other in the arms, they swayed a bit, they spat on the ground, they hocked, hollered, snorted, giggled, pushed, slapped. Danger oozed from every pore of the trio, a roaming pack in the grinding night, walking through Temple Bar, looking every woman up and down, assessing them, marking them out of ten, whistling at them, blowing kisses, standing in the way of some, *Give us a kiss love, Gowan, Nice arse baby, Lash you outta it I would*. A couple walked in the path of the boys, Spanish tourists, tanned, tipsy, lovers, holding hands, the girl, olive skinned and dark haired, smouldering with attraction, the boy taut, toned, Mediterranean model looks. Dean and the boys zoned in on the targets for fun, stopped in front of the couple:

Story, gorgeous, not you pal, yer bird, where yiz from?

Gonna ride the hole of her tonight are yuh?

She not want a bit of Irish in her, a bit of the aul Dublin meat wha?

Two Irish lads walked over to the scene, rugby players, from Trinity College,

Ah, lads, here leave it out, that's enough now, the girl's getting a fright, let them go on their way would yuhs?

Bleeding Batman and Robin is here to save the day wha? We're only having a laugh yiz fucking saps yiz.

The Spanish couple took the opportunity to get away from the encounter, and hurried off down the road, not really understanding what went on.

See yiz, now, give her one for us, yeah!

The two Rugby boys shook their heads and motioned to walk away.

Yeah, go on, fuck off that way yiz muppets, wankers, bleeding steroid heads, the state of yiz, some cheek yiz have, when yuh think of the things you Rugby boys get up to with a few drinks in yiz, said the boys.

One of the rugby lads turned and walked back and said:
Fuck you, little scrawny dirt bags.
A bottle across the head, glass shattered, kicked in the balls, punched in the face. The other Rugby lad ran over swung a punch, hit Tricky in the side of the head, wobbled him. Dean pulled out his blade, jabbed the Rugby lad in the side, jab, jab, jab, the other Rugby lad was on the ground, getting kicked and stomped on his head; he went out, his face a bloody mess. The stabbed Rugby boy clutched his side, blood seeping through his shirt on to his hand. Tricky recovered, ran over and cracked the lad full in the face with a fist, right on the jaw—the lad went to one knee. Chunk volleyed him in the chin and the lad flopped on to his back. Girls screamed, lads shouted that's enough, leave it out. Sirens, a doorman rushed to break it up. Dean and the boys scarpered like wild snarling dogs. The hunt over, satiated with blood and violence, they retreated back to St. Matthews Gardens on the north side of Dublin, to hide out.

Dean Baker, he'd put Super Glue in yer hair, piss in yer beer, send dick pics to yer girlfriend's phone, trip you as you walked, steal yer car for a laugh, drive off with it to Bray for the day.

Dean Baker, demon child, brutalised brain, mind full of vipers and black widow spiders. Dean Baker, a wrong un, brought up with fists and boots, fatherless child, council estate concrete soul, street child, falling from the light for too long. Dean Baker, what made thee such a beastly child, what made thee to walk amongst the civilised? If thou hadst been born at sea, or cast unto the Spartans of old, wouldst thou have been different, and not born to this new century, here with us? What made thee, Deano, what made thee as thou art, now? Some darkness at the edge of the Kingdom, creeping towards the centre, trailing bodies, trees, cities in its wake?

Moya Roddy

grew up in a working-class area of Dublin and left school at seventeen. The idea of becoming a writer was not on the radar, but after going to London and doing Media Studies at a Poly, she decided to give it a go. What also compelled her was the fact she never came across anyone like herself in the books she read. Her first novel *The Long Way Home* about a young working-class woman who dreams of becoming a dress designer was described in the *Irish Times* as 'simply brilliant'. Her short story collection *Other People* (Wordsonthestreet) was nominated for the Frank O'Connor Award. She's been shortlisted for the Hennessy Award and her debut collection *Out of the Ordinary* (Salmon) was shortlisted for the Strong Shine Award. Her work has been broadcast on RTE Radio and Television and on Channel 4.

They also serve who only...

Who on earth could it be at this hour, Maeve Cummins wonders, as the doorbell chimes? Picking up a tray of scones she's just finished making, she shoves them in the oven. When she was younger she'd have had an apple pie in there as well, already bubbling—she couldn't bear wasting a hot stove—these days she hasn't the heart. She'll have a couple of the scones later with her elevenses; they taste better the first day; the rest can go in the freezer once they've cooled. The bell goes again and, after checking the temperature, she tiptoes out to the bottom of the hallway, peers anxiously through the frosted glass of the front door. She's not expecting anyone, and Annie won't be arriving with her midday meal for ages. She can see by the shape it's a man, so she's not going to open it anyway; if it was someone she knew they'd have phoned.

As she slips back into the kitchen it dawns on her it could be one of the protesters. In case it is, she slips into the living-room, turns the telly up; that way if they sidetrack her later on her way to the shops she can say she didn't hear them. It wouldn't be a lie either, with the volume up you can't hear yourself thinking. It was Loretta from the new flats who told her one of them had called on her the previous day. Very well-spoken apparently; enquiring whether Loretta would like to join the picket. They have a rota would you believe! Well, whoever's on the other side of the door has another thing coming if they think she's going to stand on a picket line. What would the neighbours say, even if her legs were up to it. Which they aren't—not with varicose veins like champagne corks. According to Loretta they want to involve more local people. It makes sense, she'd explained, the more locals the better—gives it legitimacy. Maeve hadn't been too sure what that meant, and she hadn't advertised her ignorance either by asking.

They've been out there a full week, she thinks, returning to the kitchen. In all sorts of weather. Supposed to be summer, but here that's only winter by another name! She thinks she spotted Mrs. Byrne from round the corner and the good-looking husband of the couple who moved into number 21 recently. She couldn't be sure; she doesn't like to gawk as she hurries past. And she doesn't walk slowly for fear one of them might make a beeline for her. Not that they're pushy. Handing out leaflets mostly. She took one the first day out of politeness; can't remember what she did with it. Water charges! Nothing wrong with that; they shouldn't be allowed. Especially not in Ireland, she snorts, running the tap a moment before filling the kettle. Isn't water bucketing out of the heavens no matter what season it is? Coming down in the stuff we are and now they want to charge for it. A gift of God, nature anyway. And Loretta had told her we pay for it already in our taxes or PRSI or whatever. There's no flies on her; studies things although she never went further than her Inter Cert. Maeve herself has never had any time for politics or politicians; she'd love to see them trying to live on the excuse for a pension she gets. Opening the tea caddy she puts a spoon of leaves in the pot. Hard to believe she's retired seven years. Talking of flies what was that her uncle used to say? *Time flies but you can't!* It used to make her laugh. Dead now, God rest him. That put an end to his flying. Turning off the oven, she takes out the scones, arranges them on a rack. The bell goes again but when she checks whoever it was is already leaving. Funny the way people often give the bell a last ring just as they're going, she thinks, nipping into the sitting-room to get a look, see if she's right.

Maeve scrutinises the man loping up the path. He's a nice-looking fella, youngish. Why isn't he working, she wonders? All the same, he could be tucked up in bed or down the bookies instead of wearing out shoe leather walking in circles. A few Water Charges people were interviewed on the *Six O'Clock* News the night before—not those from around here—they were from Cork; groups seem to be springing up all over the country. She supposes it's a good thing—people standing up for things. Somebody has to. A couple of them on the telly were from other countries, you could tell. Probably came here thinking the very least you'd get is free water. Nothing's free, her father always said, someone has to pay for it. He'd wink when he said it and she knew he meant people like them; not the rich, who in his books paid for nothing.

Back in the kitchen, she lathers butter on two of the scones and, pulling a chair up to the table, pours the brew into her favourite cup. She tries to make a bit of a ritual of her elevenses; after all the years at work, it gets lonely here on her own; mornings drag especially and little treats help. As she indulges, she tries to remember the first time she heard about charging for water, not 'water charges' but the time they started bottling the stuff and selling it. Someone, Colette Ryan most likely, she was always showing off about going abroad, had gone to France on holiday and been gobsmacked when she'd ordered a glass of water with her bit of lunch and they'd put it on the bill. It seemed French people had taken to it like ducks to water! At the time, they'd had a good laugh, joking how they could all become millionaires overnight. That must have been the seventies. Of course, they'd all swore they'd never buy any. Pay for water, how are ye! Now look! Hundreds of different kinds too. It's the same with tea, she thinks, taking a gulp; once upon a time there was only Liptons or Lyons; these days you wouldn't know what to be asking for. She's not sure when she started buying water herself; maybe after she got a taste off the stuff coming out of the tap. No doubt on account of the chemicals used to purify it; poisoning us most likely! She read at the hairdressers that God knows how many people have already drunk the water you're drinking and—hard to credit—even after it's flushed down the toilet it's re-used. Mind you, if she really believed that she'd never let another drop past her lips. Bottled water used to taste lovely, in the beginning anyway. Of course, someone always has to spoil things; telling her the plastic seeps into the water and you're actually drinking plastic. Nothing's safe, she thinks. There's all this talk of progress yet things seem worse. How can you explain that? Like the recent outbreak of cryptosporidium. There were never problems with water when she was young. To give them their due the Council set up a lorry with a huge tank down at the Green, but it was always running out. Of course, supermarkets made a killing. It's an ill wind; all you saw was women carrying five litre bottles, one in each hand. She had to carry it herself, the thin handles nearly taking the skin off her. It taught her to appreciate water that's for sure. Made her think about those African women who have to travel miles to a well—all day sometimes—then carry those great big pitchers on their heads. Amazing. Beautiful really: the poise. She wonders how they manage, maybe it's easier once you get used to it. Ye don't see men carrying water in documentaries; they know what's good for them.

Maeve jolts up from the settee. For a split second, she's not sure where she is, stares blindly around the room, blinking her eyes. This has begun to happen: drifting off after lunch, gone to another zone. Getting up slowly, she feels for her slippers. She'll make a nice pot of tea, settle her stomach. Maeve scoops up the carton her lunch came in—vegetable lasagne—drops it in the washing basin. She'd have enjoyed it more if Annie hadn't let slip the Council were discussing doing away with the service. That took the edge off her appetite, she thinks, plugging in the kettle. They always find money for other things, she fumes, running water to wash the few dishes in the sink. When the doorbell goes, she's deep in a daydream and it gives her a start. Grumbling, Maeve dries her hands on a tea towel; hopes it isn't that protester again.

'Yes?'

Maeve peers at the young woman hovering awkwardly in the porch, a kettle dangling from her hand.

'Sorry to bother you, Mrs. I'm with the people over at the protest and we were wondering if you'd let us have some water for tea? That's a bit of a joke, isn't it—asking for water! The person supposed to bring it didn't show up—'

'That's alright—give me that yoke. I'll be back in a minute. Wait here.'

Although it seems rude, Maeve shuts the door behind her. You can't be too careful these days, she tells herself, on her way to the kitchen. They'll be asking me to join now she muses as the kettle fills up; this is only an excuse to get talking to me: wheedle me into it. For a moment, Maeve sees herself handing out leaflets, shouting 'No Water Charges! No Water Charges!' every few minutes, walking in circles, round and round. She gives herself an imaginary pinch. Who is she kidding? She'd as soon fly to the moon.

'There you are,' she says, handing over the kettle. 'Hang on. Aren't you one of the Tracey's?'

'Yeah, Trish is me mother. She's coming along later to join us.'

'Here we go!' Maeve braces herself, ready with her answer.

'I'm called Trish as well. They must have been running out of names! Thanks for the water. Me tongue's hanging out.'

'You're more than welcome. Enjoy it.'

Maeve remains at the door, an expectant look on her face. The girl grins back at her. 'Well, thanks again.'

Her eyes follow her up the path, the kettle stuck out in front of her.

'Say hello to your mother for me,' she calls.

The girl nods, shuts the gate behind her.

'Hey!' Maeve shouts, stepping into the porch. 'Anytime you need water—it's no problem. Just drop over.'

'Wait 'til they start charging for it!'

'You're right. Well, goodbye.'

'Bye—thanks again.'

As Maeve closes the door, a wave of disappointment sweeps through her. She was so sure they were going to ask her to join in. Why hadn't they? They'd asked Loretta. She catches a glimpse of herself in the hall mirror. Probably think she's too old. What did it matter anyway: she'd no intention of joining in. All the same, she'd have liked to have been asked.

Maeve turns off the telly. She's gone right off that show. Tired of it. As she heads up the stairs for bed she's aware of a weight sitting on her chest. Something's been bothering her all afternoon, ever since the Tracey girl called. Don't be acting like a spoiled child, she scolds herself, just because they didn't ask you. Reaching to turn off the light, she realises that's not the only reason. She's lonely. Apart from Loretta once in a blue moon, and Annie when she comes with the meals, she hardly speaks to a soul. It was different when she worked at the shop. There was always someone to have a chat with. The road's changed too; a lot of people have sold up and moved. She doesn't know half her neighbours, she sighs, drifting off to sleep.

When Maeve wakes next morning the weight in her chest is still there. She feels no interest in getting up: what's there to get up for? The same old, same old, day in, day out. It's not living, she thinks, there's no purpose to it. Listlessly, she stares up at the ceiling, noticing a crack she hadn't seen before. As her eyes trace it an idea begins to take shape.

As soon as breakfast is finished, Maeve gets out her baking equipment. Crumbling the flour and marg, she remembers a packet of glacé cherries she's been saving since Christmas, throws them into the mixture. After rolling out the dough, she uses a cup to cut out shapes, pops the baking tray in the oven. As she shuts the door gently she says a quick prayer they'll rise, do her proud.

It's just getting on for eleven o'clock as Maeve puts a clean tea towel over the scones, slips on her outdoor shoes. She hesitates at the door, suddenly shy, conscious someone might see her. What do I care, she suddenly thinks? At my age, I can do what I like.

Holding her breath, Maeve approaches the little knot of protesters. There's about a half-dozen of them, all ages. See, she tells herself, they're ordinary looking; no one's going to take a bite out of her.

Gingerly, she holds out the plate. 'I thought youse might like a few scones to go with your cuppa. I just made them, they're still hot.'

'Manna from heaven,' says a man wearing a silly bobble hat, raising his eyes to heaven.

'They look gorgeous,' the woman beside him adds, greedily.

'I hope they're alright. They've got cherries as well as raisins.'

In no time at all the plate is empty.

'That was very kind of you,' a tall woman who seems to be in charge thanks her.

'No bother. I could drop some over tomorrow. If you like.'

'Are ye kidding! You can take the order now.'

Maeve heads back across the road, heart swelling, blood pumping like mad around her body. She's never felt—what?—so alive. Alive and useful. As she lets herself in the front door she smiles. Tomorrow morning can't come quickly enough.

Seamus Scanlon

I was raised in the working-class redoubt of Old Mervue. The Gardai disrupted street games. Traveller horses walked through the streets—majestic and wild. We were majestic and wild.

My father worked ten hours a day, six days a week. It nearly killed him. On Sunday he brought us on walks to Salthill. Those nearly killed us. When he retired, his pension was pitiful. The abuse of the working class was in full effect. He didn't attend secondary school. My mother couldn't afford college. They instilled in us that education was a way out and a strong and abiding social justice streak.

Now I work in the Centre for Worker Education, founded in 1981 by organised labour so members could attend college, including first generation college goers (like myself) and first generation immigrants. Working with them, I imagine my parents—aiming to do better—aiming to escape poverty—aiming to escape incipient injustice. See www.ccny.cuny.edu/cwe

On the House

It was a rainy day in Galway. Nothing new—Galway and rain are synonymous, along with fog, mist, hailstones, slippery footpaths, pneumonia. The canals, the docks, the Atlantic, Nimmo's Pier, the Corrib, and Woodquay—watery graves for all tastes: for boys who wanted to be girls, for girls, young and big bellied; for women fecund with malignancies; for men uplifted by big black angels.

I was in Babe's for a haircut. My mother usually shaved mine, but she had the palsy after a week drinking Pernod. She smelt like an aniseed graveyard. I could not wait until she recovered—I had it cut every last day of the month, regardless of circumstances.

Babe's was a misnomer—a no-frills barbershop on Dominick Street, adjacent to the Eglinton Canal. Originally opened by Babe Mullaney in 1948, it was now operated by her son Brian. Everyone called him Babe in affection for his deceased mother. He was a bouncer at Seapoint and the Hangar on the weekends when he wasn't cutting hair. He didn't drink or smoke—just cut the ground from under all types of miscreants, knocking them out of their shoes and into the middle of the following week.

Maybe Babe's name in the window misled the robber. He burst in on a cash-rich Saturday evening and faltered just inside the door. He probably expected a blue-rinse brigade. But he was committed. He had a Dublin accent, which explained why he didn't know about the clientele or Babe's reputation.

He pulled a Luger from his overcoat and said, 'Don't fucking move.' All the customers apart from me were soldiers or boxers or criminals or Travellers. Everyone looked over at Babe, who was holding a pair of scissors in one hand and a comb in the other and looking sedately back at the gunman.

'Come on,' the gunman said. 'Give me the money.'

'You told us not to move,' Babe said.

'Okay, right—fuck—okay. You—you can move. Get me the money.'

The gunman covered us with a slow, unsteady gun arc. Babe put down the scissors and dropped the comb on the floor, which he bent to retrieve. As he came up, he punched the gunman so quickly and so hard that he was unconscious before he hit the wall mirror and collapsed on the floor. The mirror broke, and shards cascaded onto the tiled floor, which was seven year's bad luck for him right there. At least.

Babe stepped over the prone gunman and put the Luger in his pocket. He kept trimming the customer's hair as he went. Babe's apprentice Leper (real name Martin Leeper) locked the front door.

The gunman started to come around. He looked up at us. His eyes pleading, tears-wise. He was bleeding nose- and ears-wise. He saw only deep predator stares coming back. A fusillade of boots met him. He passed out again. Leper tied his hands with flex-cuffs.

Babe poured a jug of water on the gunman's bruised and bloody face. He was semiconscious now. Babe grabbed him by the hair and scalped him with an open razor. That woke him up, I can tell you.

Babe tore the scalp free from the remaining connective tissue and stuffed it into the gunman's mouth, and then broke his jaw so he could not dislodge it. The gunman was having trouble breathing already. Leper grabbed shorn hair from the floor and stuffed it up the guy's nostrils. Panic lit up his semi-shut eyes.

Then Babe lit the hair. His nose partly melted. The smell was appalling.

Babe lifted the guy off the floor, checked his pockets, and took out a fat bankroll.

'The fucking eejit had money already.'

Babe gestured at the back door. Leper opened it, and Babe dragged the gunman outside. We heard a low grunt, then a splash, as the guy hit the cold black water of the Eglinton Canal. He would be carried out to the Atlantic into the deep dark channels.

Babe came back and locked the door. He held up the bankroll.

'The haircuts are on the house!'

Geri Slevin

was born on a hooker off the Galway coast. She grew up in the Phoenix Park, Dublin, where her father worked as an embassy driver. The family moved to a Dublin council estate when Geri was fourteen. Her first job was in a sewing factory, when she received a letter that would change her life—awarded a full scholarship to an exclusive Dublin boarding school, paving her way to university.

Her mother, a Connemara woman, never settled in Dublin and always spoke Irish. Geri speaks four languages. Having worked professionally in theatre and film production internationally, she is the artistic director of Just4Kids theatre company. She has written several plays for children. Other works include *Invisible Woman* a play set in Armagh Gaol during the troubles. She has lived mostly on boats, and when not on land, she can be found on her lake boat The Gráinne Mhaol.

Sea Gypsy

She opened the laptop her granddaughters had given her for Christmas. At ninety-five, she felt proud. She could use this new technology, this new way of communication with the world. She typed in the password. 'This password is incorrect' flashed up on the screen. She tried again and once more 'This password is incorrect' appeared.

It would be another hour before the nice young care assistant would pop in to check on her. All the staff wore PPE gowns and surgical masks. The masks made it impossible to read lips; Gráinne was now wearing two hearing aids and the face shields blurred speech. WhatsApping was the easiest way to communicate. No password necessary. But she was out of credit and the WiFi signal was down—maybe that's why the password didn't work. Maybe it was what they called a connectivity problem.

She leaned over to the bedlocker, picked up the remote for the TV and switched on the news. She channel hopped RTE1/BBC/CNN/RT/SKY/EURONEWS. Every day now the news was bad. A virus called Covid-19, a lethal form of pneumonia, was making its way around the world with devasting consequences. Nursing homes were having huge numbers of deaths. Thirty-five people had died in a home in the next county. Gráinne never imagined dying in a place like this, ending her days in a nursing home. But after the 2008 global financial crash, the last of her family emigrated to Australia for work and a new life. Gráinne knew all about emigating and new starts. She had done it many times. She had never really settled anywhere. She was what they called Downunder a sea gypsy.

She missed the sea, the smell of the water, its colours and reflections of the huge sky above.

She was such a long way from where she had been born. She always thought the sea would take her. Ninety-five years ago, she had been born

186

on a Bád Mór between Inis Meán and Rossaveel on a beautiful sunny July morning. It was a calm crossing; her mother had gone into labour early. The whole family were leaving the island for good and moving to the mainland where there would be more work for her father and brothers, who were boat builders.

July is the water sign in the zodiac calendar and its symbol is the crab, an animal that can live on land and in water. Gráinne never felt right too far from water. No matter where she had lived in the world, she lived beside it or on it. Mostly on it. Barges in Utrecht and Paris, the old sailboat in Finiki, Turkey, and the beautiful houseboat in Marin county on the other side of the Golden Gate Bridge. In Alaska and Norway, during the fishing season, she lived right on the harbour looking out to sea.

She always got nervous and claustrophobic if she was too far from her natural habitat. Like the time she drove across Nevada or Morocco. On both those occssions, she thought out of the desert she'd never get. But that was a long time ago. The nursing home felt like those deserts. A sterile emptiness surrounded by death. One valley in Nevada was named Death Valley. Hell itself on earth.

Gráinne imagined the one thing heaven had, was plenty of water. Rivers, lakes canals, giant oceans, waterfalls, all gushing and breathing life itself. The very pulse of planet earth. Her heart beat her moods in all their wonderful complexities. Water gave Gráinne an inner sense of harmony with the world.

She switched off the TV and closed her eyes. Memories passed like an old movie, frame by frame, not unlike switching channels with the TV remote. Memory hopping. She remembered the day she left for Dublin. She hadn't wanted to leave. Her Auntie Nora had got her a job in a sewing factory. Broken-hearted she had stepped onto the Galway bus with her little brown suitcase. Her mother had splashed her with holy water from Lourdes to protect her. She waved to her brothers as the bus pulled off, biting back the tears. She looked out the window at the bay sparkling in the early morning sun. Had she been a boy she could have stayed. She had had big dreams of going to secondary school, which wasn't free in those days. But she had planned working on the fishing boats to pay the fees. Eucation back then was an expensive business. She could fish and row as good as any man and better than some of her brothers. She thought of Gráinne O'Malley. She wished her father was more like her namesake's father. She had been named Gráinne after the infamous 16th century pirate, who had visited Queen Elizabeth in London to plead for her sons' lives. A brave, independent woman and great mariner.

She had never dreamed of going to Dublin to work in a factory making clothes. She had wanted an education. How many times had she heard her mother say the most important thing in life for a girl was to get an education. She had heard it so often over the years 'You'll never be independent if you're financially dependent on a man. Men don't need an education to earn money. They can work on building sites, drive trucks, fish. But for a woman it's different, Gráinne, you need an education to get on.' Yet, here she was just turned fourteen, and on the bus to Dublin to work in a factory. When the bus turned the corner at Mac Con Iomaire's shop and post office, the family still waving disappeared from view.

She thought about the hooker races she was going to miss this year. In July, the villages of Kilkieran, Cashel, Mac Dara island, Roundstone and Lettermullen hosted the best races. She would miss the hoisting of the beautiful russet sails, the foghorn signalling the start of the race and that exciting feeling as the boat keeled sharply, approaching the first buoy race marker. Nowdays, the Galway hookers had become an icon. It is the emblem on the county crest, an ale had been named after it, and the Galway Hooker Association had been revived. The old work boats of her childhood were suddenly centre stage, and when the Volvo Ocean Race came to Galway a flotilla of hookers greeted them.

So many memories the boats carried. She remembered her grandmother knitting the natural wool, off-white Aran sweaters for her dad and brothers, a simple cable stitch that looked like the hooker ropes and was so scratchy against her skin.

Another memory floated up of how the boats were used to move the men on the run during the Civil War. Her cousin Seamus O'Malley had crossed the lake to meet up with his friends in Headford when they were arrested, charged for possession of a rifle and ammunition, and sentenced to death. Seamus and his friends had been part of the Oughterard Battalion of the 4th Western Division of the IRA. On the 11th of April 1923 Seamus and his friends were taken to Tuam Military Barracks (Workhouse) and executed by firing squad. He was twenty years old.

The war came to an end a few weeks later, in May. Gráinne's aunt never got Seamus's body back till the following October, when he was handed over in a ceremony at Athlone Barracks where the bodies had been moved when Tuam Barracks closed. He was laid to rest in the Republican plot in the graveyard in Oughterard.

Another frame of her life flashed past. She remembered her cousin the boat builder from Lettermullen. Now a lovely marble plaque commemorated the boat builders between 1840 and 1983. Again, she thought of her dad and her brothers. She missed them all even after all these years. They were true craftsmen and built beautiful boats. She remembered them tarring the small currach she fished in as a young girl, its smell making her vomit. Gráinne was good at fishing. When the mackerel were running, she could just drop a piece of string overboard with several hooks attached and she'd bring home buckets full for her mother to salt in the brown wooden barrels. She loved this little silvery, tasty fish.

She remembered her first halibut, caught off Homer's Spit at the tip of the Kenai Penninsula in Alaska, jutting out into Kachemak Bay. Bald eagles sat patiently on the pylons in the small harbour. The Spit was the longest road into ocean waters in the entire world and took twenty minutes to drive across. It's also where the boats leave to take crew out to Dutch Harbour for crab season. Made famous by the TV reality show the *Deadliest Catch*, Gráinne never missed an episode; many of the captains were sons of old friends. Halibut was the giant of flatfish and chief food source for native Alaskans and Canadian First Nation peoples. She had heard once on the news a whopper measuring eight metres and weighing in at 235 kilos had been caught in Norwegian waters.

She remembered evenings in the Salty Dawg Saloon and her first big pay share. She felt rich and she gave the barman an old Irish ten-shilling note (the paper the same colour as the king crabs and the hooker sails) to tack onto the wall behind the bar. She was one of very few female crew in Alaskan waters. Everyone knew her and she was treated as one of the lads, a hardworking, fearless, no-nonsense fisherwoman who could throw a line with unerring accuracy and was a good cook when in the galley.

She remembered the book she had brought with her on one of the fishing trips, Walter Macken's *Rain on the Wind*. He wrote about her people, their story of constant struggle with the unpredictable sea, with poverty and with the political conservatism of post-independent Ireland.

It was 2020, and Ireland still wasn't free. She was going to die without seeing a united Ireland and she felt a deep sadness. 'Gráinne are you all right? can I do anything for you?' Her favourite care assistant had just come into her room. 'You can, peteen. Can you help with my password?'

Andy Snoddy

was born and raised in East Belfast and at sixteen began work as an apprentice printer. Aged twenty-three, Andy was elected as a full time union official for the printers union the GPMU. An active trade unionist, he was the Secretary of Belfast Trades Council and a member of the Northern Ireland Committee of the ICTU. Since then, he has worked abroad mainly in the area of organising for different trade unions, GPMU, UNITE in Britain, 3F in Denmark and is currently the Head of Organising for UNI Global Union based in Nyon in Switzerland. Throughout his life he has been active in left politics and a member of the Connolly Youth Movement, CPI, Labour Coalition, Respect, Enhedslisten (in Denmark) and is currently a member of the Vaud executive Committee of POP, the Swiss workers' party.

The Radical Protestant Tradition
A Letter to My Grandchildren

Dear Lark, Margot, Indigo, Ada and Ren

I am writing to tell you a story about our family, which you will be able to read when you are a bit older. You are growing up in Northern Ireland, where sectarian tensions still exist. Sometimes these are open, sometimes below the surface, where people will classify you. As you are not Catholics, they think you must be Protestants, and if you are Protestant, you must be unionist. Lark, Margot and Ren, you are living in East Belfast where some of what I am about to tell you took place. Ada and Indigo, you are living in Saintfield, where in 1798 the mainly Presbyterian United Irishmen defeated the English Redcoats.

In my possession is a book, one of the volumes of *The Cabinet of Irish Literature*, published between 1879 and 1888. It belonged to my great uncle and his name is written, in Gaelic script, on the inside cover, Séamus Mac Snadaigh 1916.

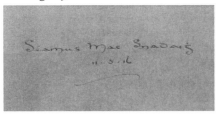

I have often wondered how my great uncle James Snoddy, a Methodist from the Lower Ormeau Road, became Séamus Mac Snadaigh, an Irish speaking member of the Irish Volunteers, who, alongside the Irish Citizens Army, were to launch the 1916 Rebellion.

James was born in 1888, the first of two sons, the other being my grandfather John. In the 1901 census, he is listed as an English speaker, but by 1911 the census records him as an Irish speaker. He clearly learnt Irish during this period and I guess it probably was a first step towards his radical republican politics.

The Irish language has become increasingly politicised in recent years, in a negative way and in a manner that has tended to polarize attitudes towards it, especially among unionists. However, *Hidden Ulster* by Padraig O Snodaigh (a distant relative) shows that many of the Ulster Protestant planters in the 16th and 17th centuries were Gaelic speakers. It is a tradition that continues to this day with Linda Ervine's language classes on the Newtownards Road in East Belfast. It would be no surprise for many attending these classes to learn that the Unionist Party, in 1905, at one of its conventions, proudly displayed a banner in Irish, openly and for all to see, without any shame or embarrassment.

The Gaelic League was founded in 1892, by a Protestant, Douglas Hyde, and quickly spread across Ireland. Hyde believed that the language should be politically neutral. In 1905, he said, 'The Irish language, thank God, is neither Protestant nor Catholic, it is neither a Unionist nor a Separatist.'

The first branch of Conradh na Gaeilge (The Gaelic League) in Belfast was founded in 1895 by Dr John St Clair Boyd, a paediatric surgeon. Boyd was a member of the Church of Ireland. The inaugural meeting was held at 32 Upper Beersbridge Road in East Belfast, and Boyd was elected first chairperson of this branch. Your granny Karen and I lived for a number of years off the Beersbridge Road, just a stone's throw from where my great uncle most likely learned his Irish. How he became a republican is not so clear, but I suspect Bulmer Hobson must have played a part.

Hobson was an old friend of my own granny, your great great granny, Emily Snoddy. She was from County Armagh as was Bulmer Hobson's family. Both were Quakers and both attended the Friends' School in Lisburn. I can remember visiting him on our way to County Kerry for a summer holiday with my granny when I was seven or eight years old. My granny told me the story that, when Bulmer was caught doodling at school and ordered in front of the class to show everyone what he had drawn, this was a postage stamp for when Ireland was independent. Later, when Hobson was deeply involved with nationalist movements, he resigned on principle from the Quakers, due to their opposition to all forms of violence.

My granny claimed that he went on to be Postmaster General of the Irish Free State.

They say you should never let the truth get in the way of a good story. A little research shows, as Emily was younger, there would only have been a few years overlap in their time at the Friends' School. Therefore, it would seem unlikely if not impossible, that they shared the same classroom. And while Bulmer Hobson was not Postmaster General, he was a civil servant in the Department of Post and Telegraphs after Independence.

As the school anecdote illustrates, Hobson was a maverick from early on. Aged thirteen, he subscribed to the nationalist journal *Shan Van*

Vocht, and in the late 1890s he joined the Belfast Branch of the Gaelic League. That is probably where he met Séamus Mac Snodaigh.

We don't know if Hobson recruited Séamus Mac Snodaigh into the Volunteers, but as Volunteers from Belfast they must have known each other. By 1915, if not before, Séamus Mac Snodaigh was himself recruiting people into the Irish Volunteers. Séamus is also recorded as the organizer of a meeting after a Volunteer target (shooting) practice event at a gravel pit in Rosenna, County Laois in August 1914. Two other members of the Snoddy family, Sam and Patrick, from Carlow, were also listed as being in attendance. So, 130 years ago your great great great uncle was over 160 miles away from his home in Protestant East Belfast, deep in the Midlands of Ireland, organizing Irish Volunteers.

In Easter week 1916, the 130 strong Belfast contingent of Volunteers were mobilised to meet with the Tyrone Volunteers in Coalisland and then to proceed to link up with Liam Mellows in Galway. Was Séamus there? He is not on the list of Volunteers. Perhaps he missed the mobilization, or opposed the Rising, like Hobson. We may never know.

Lark, Margot, Indigo, Ada and Ren, when you read this, you will know that I penned this little family memoir for you during the great Covid-19 pandemic of 2020. As far as I know, Séamus Mac Snodaigh never wrote down his thoughts on all this for future generations. I would have loved to read them. Unfortunately, he died aged only thirty, in the flu epidemic in 1919, a hundred and one years ago, and forty years before I was born.

Ross Walsh

is a freelance journalist and poet based in Ireland. He has been writing poetry and fiction for over ten years. Born in Wexford, he has spent a lot of his time in the North of Donegal or by the sea in Wexford and Waterford, where he was immersed in the working-class traditions of these areas. The landscape and scenery of these places has also inspired much of the imagery in his writing. He recently returned to Ireland from New York City, where he experienced first-hand the devastating effect the COVID-19 pandemic is having on the city's working-class residents. Like many others, he found himself out of work and struggling to survive in the city, prompting his return to Ireland.

King of the Concrete Jungle

Even a silent city is never truly quiet. The echoes of millions of voices have soaked into the concrete and steel. You can hear it in the groaning of skyscrapers, their foundations struggling like Atlas to hold up the weight bearing down on them. They live on, somewhat, in the cracking of the pavement and the shattering of glass windows by roots and branches, growing without fear of retribution for the destruction they unintentionally cause. They make their presence known in the lapping of the waves on rotting piers, the gurgling of newborn rusted holes in the sides of pleasure yachts. They gasp for air and find only the salty, frigid water pulling the boats down. These are only echoes, though. Not voices. Not the shouting, calling, screaming, yelling, cajoling, hawking, and cursing that once filled the streets. The decaying city releases its quiet whispers, but the whispers have no throats they emerge from.

Wolf does not care for the whispers. The slow collapse of the concrete jungle means nothing to him. He knows not that these sounds echo around the empty streets because there are no humans left to tend their metropolitan garden; he only understands that there are no humans here anymore. Sniffing at the deflated tires of what was once an expensive sports car, he cannot comprehend that these metal shells once glided down bustling avenues with enough speed to crush every bone in his body if they made contact. After all, Wolf was born in a world surrounded by the bark of towering trees, not the bricks and mortar of townhouses. He does not ask how he came to be here, a world both frozen in time and crumbling under its assault. He left the forest of his youth and, as wolves are wont to do, he roamed.

The city is not so different from the forest that shaped him as a pup, not anymore. Where once he listened for the creaking and groaning of rotting trees, whose branches were about to snap and fall where he stood, now the street lights and scaffolding make the same noises before gravity thrusts them down. There was a time when the cloven hooves of deer broke twigs and alerted Wolf to their location, from where he could pick up their scent. Now they scatter discarded aluminium cans, the sound bouncing along the streets like gunshots. Hunting is much easier in the city.

A natural order, of sorts, has emerged here. The wolves mix with the feral dogs that survived, forming packs, tracking and feasting on the deer that roam the parks, dotted between the skeletons of corporate headquarters and slum tenements. The rats own the underground. Breeding, multiplying, stripping any animal unwise enough to venture below to the bone. Wolf does not know what a subway station is, but he knows they stink of rot, mould, excrement and blood.

Wolf has no pack. Not yet. The city is large, vast, and he has yet to find a lonely she-wolf to hunt with. So for now he hunts alone. His light grey fur almost blends into the dull grey walls as he roams the streets, waiting for a scent to assail his nose, or the clanging of an aluminium can to reach his ears. His amber eyes scan ahead, alert for the slightest movement. He ignores the pigeons cooing as they strut along the disintegrating concrete. Wolf would not know, but those birds have not changed much at all. They always strutted, even when humans strutted alongside them, man and bird both acting as though they had important places to be.

A soft crackling draws Wolf's attention. It is coming from what was once a bar, the windows long smashed and the door trying and failing to cling to its hinges. His huge paws tread softly over the broken shards as he skulks inside, sniffing cautiously at the stagnant air. The lights are out, and have been longer than Wolf has roamed the city. Some of the liquor bottles lining the wall are still intact. Others have broken under the elements, their contents soaking into the worn wood of the bar and leaving the smell of alcohol to linger longer than it had any right to. Although it was not nearly enough to mask the strongest smell there: the stench of death.

The bones of former patrons lay slumped over the bar, their tattered clothes holding their skeletons together in a vague human form. Long, thin fingers still circled dusty pint glasses, many still full of alcohol. Empty eye sockets sat above the eternal grins of their skulls, as if being alive was no prerequisite to be drunk and merry. Wolf finds the source of the crackling. A small box on a shelf, with a long thin tail pointing straight up. A human would have called it a radio. A human would have also understood the words emanating from the radio, barely audible about the static.

THIS IS A LOOPING EMERGENCY BROADCAST. ALL CITIZENS MUST RETURN TO THEIR HOMES AND AVOID SOCIAL CONTACT. THE VIRUS IS SPREADING RAPIDLY, AND KILLING MORE QUICKLY THAN ANTICIPATED. PLEASE RETURN TO YOUR HOMES IMMEDIATELY. THIS IS A LOOPING EMERGENCY BROADCAST.

With no sign of any prey to hold his interest, Wolf leaves the bar. He is hungry. He ventures north, towards the big park with the most deer. Normally, he tries to avoid the big park. There are so many packs there, all fighting over territory and prey, that a lone wolf doesn't stand a chance. But hunger is the rumbling of desperation deep in his stomach, and the rumbling has been getting louder for days now. It has grown so loud that he nearly doesn't hear the clanging of the aluminium can just up ahead. Nearly.

Slowing his powerful gallop to a stealthy slink forward, he rounds a corner and sees her. A solitary doe, frozen by the noise she has made herself. Wolf begins to salivate. As he takes a step forward, the doe turns her head ever so slightly. Just enough to bring his movement into her line of vision. For what must have been eternity, they stand motionless. Both know, by instinct alone, what is about to happen. Millions of years of natural order condensing itself into a few seconds right then and there. The ethereal connection between predator and prey. Just as quickly as it begun, the spell breaks and the chase is on.

Wolf bounds after the doe, his heartbeat quickening to match his pace. They are engaging in a dance as old as time itself, even if the stage is new. They leap and twist over rusted cars and toppled trash cans, occasionally knocking aside the bleached bones of the dead. The wind blows back in Wolf's face, carrying the whispers of the city and, more powerfully, the intoxicating smell of fear from his target. Her cloven hooves pound the pavement until she jerks to the side, sprinting through the shattered remains of a glass door. He follows her inside, and continues after her as she ascends a seemingly never ending staircase.

Wolf has no sense of time as he hunts. His brain shuts out all stimuli other than the scent of the doe and the ache in his stomach. Hunter and hunted climb the stairs up and up, smashing against walls as they turn corners, gaining and losing ground in an almost intimate back and forth. The end of the stairs is finally in sight when the doe's hoof catches on the final step. The tumble would be less fatal without the sickening death knell of bone cracking in her leg. It only takes a second for Wolf to catch up, and then the dance is over.

Once he finishes satiating his hunger, Wolf ventures forth through the top floor of the skyscraper. Suddenly he finds himself outside again, with the wind lapping at his fur just like the waves on the rotting piers so many miles below. He ambles towards the edge of the deck, to the wall of glass separating him from the world. The city is sprawled out beneath him, what was once a canopy of grey now dotted with green where the trees have conquered the concrete. The whispers of the city cannot reach him up here. Looking down, the dead metropolis is truly silent for the first time. Wolf leans his head back and howls. Humans once called the lion the King of the Jungle. If they could see him now, they might call Wolf the King of the Concrete Jungle. He has no way of knowing this. He leans back and howls again.

'Liberty' by Jim Ward

Jim Ward

is a native of Salthill, Galway, and is the first of his family to go to university. From a working-class family, he achieved a scholarship and studied engineering to get a job. He has, nonetheless, experienced periods of precarious employment and unemployment—working as a hotel night porter, a factory manager, a software engineer, and drawing the dole. He is the author of the award-winning play *Just Guff* (Galway Fringe Festival, 2017), since performed at venues including Town Hall Studio, Galway and Liberty Hall, Dublin, as part of MayFest, 2019. He has published poetry and short stories in Irish and English. His poem '2016 Proclamation' was runner-up in the Thoor Ballylee/Galway Bay, FM Yeats Poetry Challenge, 2017. A history buff, he earned a Regional Tour Guide badge with Fáilte Ireland and gives entertaining walking tours of Galway city. In keeping with his precarious existence, he doesn't know if he will be getting any tours next year.

Evelyn

after James Joyce

'You're gorgeous,' Paul told her.

She did not believe him, but as she went from table to table, self-consciously smiling, walking awkwardly, a young doe, she'd catch the men looking up from their tables, feast their eyes on her then look away again when she would exchange a smile. The men, bus drivers and porters from the station round the corner, in for the carvery lunch. Solid grub of meat with potatoes and veg served with thick gravy.

She collected sloppy glasses, absent-mindedly, and plates with chewed gristle or unwanted vegetables left on them. But she'd be awoken from her dreaming by these men giving her the once over. She hadn't attracted that kind of attention before. It was all new to her and she felt both flattered and uneasy by it.

Back home in Kracow this never happened. The Railway Arms where she had landed a job as a waitress was very different from the seedy bars and musty baroque beerhalls of her home town with their whiff of desperation. Here, it was all plush carpet and refurbished provincial grandeur. Old fashioned respectability with the crude facelifts of new-found prosperity. The old photographs on the walls told her a lot.

'Ireland still has the faith,' Fr. Jerzy told her father, 'and the people the grace of God,' he added.

'A minimum wage as well,' he informed him, jerking his head forward with emphasis.

No, in Poland she never received this kind of attention. So, she walked awkwardly from table to table, trying to deflect leers, admiring or not, from the patrons.

She had no qualifications. At school the teachers had given up on her. 'Now, Evelyn, can you answer this one...?' and when she couldn't it was, 'Now just read your book to yourself, Evelyn,' as the teacher concentrated on the rest of the class. But she had learned English.

At twenty-one she did not remember the old days in her native Poland. The days of the socialist state where everybody, no matter how backward, had a job or position in society. Her father, a devout catholic, often told her about those days.

'They, the communists were bad people,' he would say. 'They had no god'. He did not like communists, though he had held a permanent job under the old regime, and under it would not have had to send his only daughter to a foreign country as he had her.

In the afternoons when the lunchtime crowd went back to work a different clientele took over. Mostly retired men with ruddy faces and bloodshot eyes. The racing on the big screen and their eyes glued to their newspapers, quietly muttering to themselves and each other, scribbling out betting chits for the neighbourhood bookie, their voices gradually getting louder as the drinks took effect. Then they joked with her. She made them feel young and desirable again. And when they got a little bit tipsy, one of them would hold her in his arms and they'd do a little set around the floor. Yes, she felt, she made them feel young again.

So, she walked awkwardly from table to table, trying to deflect leers, admiring or not, from the patrons.

She met Paul at a party. At twenty-one, she had never had a man in her life before—Mona, her best friend, often told her she should be more confident with boys—'Come on, Evelyn, boys are like putty in girls' hands.'

But she was looking for companionship and security in this new country and Paul was all the business. He was twenty-five and he even said he had his own business. She did not know what type of business he had, but he was forever answering calls to his mobile phone. His manner took on a sense of urgency whenever it would ring and he'd walk off to take the call in private. Then there was the time when he had borrowed twenty euros from her, which remained unpaid. He regularly went away. 'To England on business,' he would explain when asked.

They had not slept together yet, due to her religious convictions, and this had not deterred Paul from seeing her. She thought this was good. Then there was Paul's politics. For someone born in a country once calling itself socialist, with a father virulently anti-communist, she had made a strange relationship with a businessman who declared himself a socialist, and even brought her to some meetings.

The obscure left-wing political group he belonged to was called 'The

Irish Revolutionary Workers' Movement'. Paul insisted that they were not at all like the socialists who had governed her own country for over forty years.

'We are not Stalinists,' he would insist. 'We want a workers' and small farmers' republic for all of Ireland.' This struck her as odd. She had often heard of a workers' republic but not of a small farmers' republic as well. It must be an Irish thing, she thought, calculating it would not do to ask any questions.

For they are a child-like people, always wanting to know what others thought of them.

'How do you like our town?' they would ask. 'What do you think of our cathedral? Of our new hospital?' and so on.

And they could be downright racist too, she thought, remembering the time she heard herself and Mona called 'Polacks'.

She asked herself what would her father think, going to a socialist meeting? After all, he was one of those Poles who had resisted communism in the home country, supporting the Solidarnosc trade union, a disciple of the late Polish pope, John Paul. A man who regularly consulted Fr. Jerzy, the parish priest, before taking a course of action.

So, she walked awkwardly from table to table, trying to deflect leers, admiring or not, from the patrons.

At the meetings she attended in the American Bar, a city-centre, low rent hotel—all electric red outside and cheap fluorescent inside, about ten people in the back room argued about ways to increase membership. They called each other 'comrade' even though they knew each other's names. What struck Evelyn most was that for a group invoking the title 'Workers' Movement' none of them seemed to work a proper job to merit being called 'proletariat' or 'working class'—you see she knew something about politics. They seemed to have either no job or they called themselves writers or, like Paul, 'businessmen'. Another curious fact was that there were no female members of this progressive group. The chairman of the group, Ralph, was a grey-haired man in his late sixties she guessed. All the others were in their twenties. Paul told her that this man, the chairperson, had been politically active since the 1970s, trying to recruit volunteers to the scientifically pre-determined socialist utopian future. She remained silent, observing. Again, she did not mention that all the comrades appeared to have been born years later than the 1970s. Was it, she wondered, perseverance, determination or simply failure on his part? Maybe, she thought, they would attract more members if instead of endlessly deliberating about dogma, they campaigned on wages and conditions.

As for her, well, she was getting the minimum wage. It was tough to make ends meet week by week and still try to send money home. Sometimes she could not afford to do both. Paul had been for some time now hinting that she could make much more money if she listened to him.

'Come over to England with me next time,' he would say, spooning lots of sugar in the many black coffees he drank in the local cafés on their dates. 'I have contacts.'

He did not say for what, but mentioned working in the entertainment industry. She thought that could mean anything.

'You'd be ideal,' he told her.

She wondered whether she might accompany him. She wondered what her father might say if she upped and left for a different country. What would Fr. Jerzy back home have to say about this? She liked her present job and she knew the customers liked her, and not just because of the admiring glances, which could be scary.

So, she walked awkwardly from table to table, trying to deflect leers, admiring or not, from the patrons.

In fact, Paul said he wanted to introduce her to some special client of his. He said he would ring her mobile phone later that day to arrange a meeting, and to only answer if she was seriously intent on following him. She thought of her secure job in the bar, the friendly people with the grace of God as her parish priest had said. Would she swap all this for a precarious existence in England in what Paul had called the 'entertainment industry?' Should she ask her father before making a decision, or would she surprise him?

Just then she heard her phone ring. She looked at the number. It was Paul calling as he said he would.

The phone rang...

Would she answer...?

What would she say...?

The phone still rang...

What would she do...?

The phone rang on...

Anne Waters

We all have a connection with the 'working class', no matter how it is defined. My link, through my mother, is to the rural, farming, working class. Seventy years ago, life on a farm was harsh and shrouded in poverty and deprivation. The necessity to contribute financially was paramount. As such, her education was inevitably shortened, thus affecting job prospects and progression. Fluency in English was essential, so speaking in her native tongue was frowned upon. Social and cultural inadequacy and inferiority, are a consequence, which takes effort to overcome but is also reproduced.

The working class have been categorised according to accent, education, job, and address. Taste, attire, and posture are also considered distinguishing features. Class lines today are more blurred, but the one element that is universal is the lack of power, be it social, economic, or political.

St. Stephen's Day

It was six months since our mother passed away and opening her 'treasure box' on St. Stephen's Day seemed appropriate. For me, it was a fitting memorial, a testament to her Irishness, and the high esteem she had bestowed on the day. Mother's ritual demand that we attend Mass in the morning and light a candle was anathema to Jenny. She always insisted it was 'Boxing Day,' and with mother gone, felt no obligation to preserve any memory; thus, my sister refused to join me.

The 'treasure box' was but a shoebox, tied tightly with string, but it was always private. Every St. Stephen's Day, after our compulsory church visit, mother retired to her room and spent an hour alone. I now opened the lid of the box, excitement building, anxious to behold its secrets. To say I was disappointed is an understatement. Birth certs, old school reports, baby bangles, I just could not see what was so special, until I spied a pair of blue, baby bootees. Delicately crocheted, with tiny ribbons now slightly frayed, one little boot held a wispy fragment of soft, downy, fair hair. I held them gently, poignant in their sad simplicity, as the harsh December sunlight, streaming through the window, sketched how threadbare and faded they now were. Jenny and I were nothing but pink little girls until the age of twelve. Mystified, I determined to ascertain what mystery lay within, and instinctively was aware that Aunt Ellen would know.

Four years older than my mother, Ellen lived close by. Not blessed with children of her own, she was thoroughly involved in our rearing, almost a surrogate mother. I wrapped the little bootees in tissue paper and hurried to her house. Her usual greeting was an instant hug, but that day she halted, taken by surprise when she saw what lay in my hand. Stunned, she turned away, but not before I saw the tears well in her eyes, and slowly descend her cheeks. Her voice was thick with emotion, she prevaricated, asking if I wanted tea, perhaps some cake? Gently, I steered her back to the table. My eyes had questions; hers had answers. Taking hold of her hands, I gently massaged her gnarled fingers, silently pleading, and haltingly, hesitantly, she proceeded to tell me about a mother I never knew.

'As you know, Kate, we were reared in Donegal. I was older, but we were close and went everywhere together. You need to understand the times, what Ireland, especially Donegal, was like in the 1950s. Of course, we knew the mechanics of sex, we lived on a farm after all, but sex between a woman and a man was shrouded in secrecy. It was preserved for marriage, that was the sum total of our knowledge. We believed that everyone, including all the young men, accepted this diktat without question. Every Saturday night, we went to the Church Social.' Ellen smiled as she continued. 'The lights were always blazing so brightly, and dancing was never too close. It was normal then to have a lad walk you home, and if he had a bike, well, so much the better. The following morning, we all met again at Mass and Communion. Innocent times, how innocent we were, believing without question what we were told and accepting our assigned place. When I look back, I am still amazed at how we trusted, and never questioned the overwhelming power of the Church, that had us in thrall. Anyway, I digress.' Ellen stood abruptly, needing a moment. I sensed she made tea as a diversion before visibly gathering herself to continue.

'There was something special about Sarah. I knew, well I felt anyway, that I was attractive, and my friend Rose who lived down the lane was quite beautiful, but Sarah was something else. She was only sixteen, but when she entered a room, all the lads turned towards her, moths to a flame. It was in the swish of her hair and the swing of her hips, the curve of her smile. She was popular with all the boys, but there was jealousy among some of the girls. The future for most of us, you see, was emigration to England or America, but many girls hoped for marriage to a local lad with prospects, be it a farm or family pub. Sarah seemed to tantalise all around her, and that gave rise to a lot of spite. Yet she didn't seem to notice, she was just happy and carefree.' Ellen sipped her tea slowly, her eyes glazed, lost in a faraway time, reliving difficult and heartbreaking memories.

'It was St. Patrick's Night,' she finally whispered, 'and I just didn't feel well, with a searing headache. The dance was underway, and I told Sarah I had to go home. I knew any number of lads would see her up the laneway, and I, thankfully, sank into bed without any worries. It must have been around 2 a.m. when I was awoken by a distraught Sarah. I knew immediately what had occurred. She was covered in mud, scratched and bleeding, with tears streaming down her face. The notion of hopping into a shower didn't exist in those days, so, I crept silently into the yard and filled a bucket with cold water. I sponged her down myself while attempting to soothe her. I even stole a drop of whiskey from Dad's precious store to help her sleep. Calling the police was not even considered, just hiding the truth from our parents was all that mattered. When I think back, with today's knowledge, I can understand how and why she changed so much. There was no such thing as counselling in those days. A light just went out in Sarah, and she hung her head in shame. She said she felt grubby, that she must have led the lad on and forced him to commit sin. We were indoctrinated to believe it was always the woman who had to have control, and if she had, no man would do wrong. We also thought that losing virginity before marriage rang a death knell for the future. We were strangled by a Church's teaching, that subordinated women and blamed them for tempting men. I shudder when I think back. How my actions must have exacerbated her shame because I helped her hide.' Grasping Kate's hand, Ellen stuttered,' but Kate, you must believe me, I thought I was helping.' Silent tears of regret, of guilt, and palpable anger at a Church and society, that condemned a raped girl, and exonerated all men, slid, in an unending stream, down her cheeks.

'I was preparing to travel to London to Great Aunt Mary, but within three months, I knew Sarah had to go too. She was obviously pregnant. At only sixteen, I assumed we would have great difficulty in persuading our parents, but they agreed quite quickly. I think they must have gleaned something was amiss, but nothing was said. Shame, you see, the need to hold your head high mattered, above all else. Best to pretend Sarah was going away to work. The one thing I am thankful for is that I never tried to persuade her to name the boy. A hastily arranged marriage often happened, but usually the couple had been courting. Imagine at sixteen, being forced into a marriage with someone who had perpetrated such violence upon you? Anyway, we travelled to Dublin to meet Aunt Mary, but as soon as she laid eyes on Sarah, she knew she was expecting.' Ellen sighed deeply, pausing, before steeling herself to continue. 'Mary only meant to help, and in hindsight, there was little she could have done. She knew unmarried mothers in England fared little better than those in Ireland, so we left her in a Magdalen Laundry, in Dublin. Of course, at that time, we didn't know the reality of the 'Laundries'. We all thought the nuns were wonderful, caring for fallen, sinful women and their babies. Oh, how foolish and stupid we were.' A sigh of deep despair escaped Ellen. Drawing breath, she muttered sarcastically, 'men were blameless apparently, and at the mercy of women, all sexual sirens who seduced them against their will.'

Ellen paused. I was aware of how difficult this was for her, but every time she stopped for breath, or took a moment to process a memory, I felt a surge of impatience. It was essential I heard the full story, and as quickly as possible. 'Afterwards, I obtained a job in London and sent money home, pretending some came from Sarah. I loved London, and the only blight was the constant worry over your mother. Christmas was approaching, and I wrote and told our own mother we couldn't afford to travel home. Instead, I journeyed alone to Dublin. I was frightened and lonely, but I knew the baby was due in late December, and I had to be there for Sarah.' Ellen reached for the bootees and caressed the frayed ribbons. She sniffed the frail strands of hair, one stray wisp gently weaving around her little finger, the faded wool now sodden with her sobs. 'I made these,' she said. 'One is a bit bigger than the other, but Sarah loved them.'

'That December, I called every day to the convent and pleaded, to no avail, to be allowed to see her. It was January before they let me in. Her little boy was born on St. Stephen's Day, so she named him after the saint. Little Stephen was so beautiful, but I only held him for a few minutes. I was abruptly ordered to put him down, by a stone-faced nun, who ushered me out of the nursery.' As we held hands across the table, I understood that Ellen, herself, had never forgotten that little boy. 'Sarah worked in the laundry until the following August. She was then permitted to return to Donegal, to care for our mother, who was now very ill.' 'But what of Stephen?' I interrupted. 'Stephen?' whispered Ellen. 'Poor little Stephen just disappeared. His cot was empty one morning. Gone to a good home, they said. Sarah had no chance to say goodbye, or hold him one last time. That broke her heart and spirit.'

'Sarah nursed our mother with great care, but it was as though she was doing penance, atoning for her sins. She appeared to internalise the censure of society and genuinely felt she deserved condemnation. Poor Sarah, she never questioned the Church and their view of women, believing their denunciation was justified, and her violation was her own fault. When next we met, I could not fathom how this once bright and sparkly young girl had metamorphosed into a dull, critical, and scrupulous individual. A daily communicant, her head hung in contrition, as though by virtue of being extra devout, she could exorcise her guilt. Eventually, she married your father, but I don't believe she ever told him about Stephen. She remained half the girl I knew, until after you and Jenny were born. A light then flickered and slowly glowed, but she was never quite the same. The move to London was a help. Changing times, and a less censorious society, helped Sarah rationalise what happened. Strange to say, the death of your father helped somewhat. She had to find the strength to care for you two girls, which meant facing the world, working, and taking charge of life. Meeting new people and new situations widened her horizons and enabled her to question the teachings of a Church that had held such dominance over her.

I felt shaken, unable to absorb the imagery of a young Sarah, with the gentle, but strict and austere woman, who had been my mother, a woman of such sorrow. The revelation that I had an older brother, and that he was the treasure in Mother's box, prompted me to ask, 'Did anyone ever search for

Stephen?' Ellen shrugged her shoulders. 'No, it just was never possible. But wherever he went, he never left your mother's heart.'

Alan Weadick

Since leaving secondary school in the 1980s, Alan has worked in a wide variety of jobs across the construction, retail, health, manufacturing and security sectors, while at the same time being involved as an actor, writer and backstage in the fringe theatre scene of the 1990s. More recently, he has been publishing poetry and short stories in outlets including the *Irish Times, Cyphers, Southword* and *The Honest Ulsterman*. He was a reader at *Poetry Ireland*'s Introductions, has been long and shortlisted for competitions including Listowel Writers' Week, Strokestown Poetry Festival, the National Poetry competition (UK 2017) the Francis McManus short story competition, and been nominated for a Hennessy Literary Award (Emerging Poetry, 2016). He won the Mairtín Crawford Award for Poetry, 2020, and continues to work as a security officer in Dublin, where he lives with his wife and two children.

Transcendence

The staff presence on my floor that night was unusual, but nothing I couldn't handle. I could assume that the Irishman had never set foot in Vistulia and that the name Fontan Mentoyan meant nothing to him. I could therefore also assume that he had glanced at me vacuuming the other side of the seventh floor, thought his hundreds of thousands of euros a year thoughts, then looked down again, mentally deleting me. But, hey! The Mentoyan skin grows thicker every day; the Mentoyan soul receives not a dent.

I have been doing this work for three years now and it's not like this was the first time a member of staff had worked late on my floor in all that time. But at that stage I had nothing to report. I had no anecdotes, humorous or otherwise, like some of my colleagues in BriteCo. Services sometimes have, about their encounters with the clients.

My colleagues, with whom a minute's exchange in stilted English is sometimes possible before their always brief tours here are terminated, cut short by the error of imagining themselves less wretched than they are. Even I, a full-blooded Vistulian, son of the least invaded kingdom on the Continent of Europa till 1805 CE, Year of Ignominy, do not labour under any such illusions. We have had our shot, I try to tell them, but now it is at an end. *FINI!* I am sure that our ancestors in the days of their maximum glory also bridled under the burden of their thralls' terrible obscurity. And who could blame them? I'm sure it is an irritant, the presence of all of us culturally vague peoples performing all those manual, often intimate services they have had to divest themselves of. It has to find some kind of expression, does it not?

I myself might not go as far as to demand a worker's removal from the site with complaints about his tendency to perspire heavily while performing his duties, for example. Or, just as loudly, about another's heavy use of anti-perspirant products. There are subtler instruments, but I do understand the conflict.

Another fallen colleague shared the tale of how one senior executive here had conducted a campaign of constantly and energetically re-soiling the gents' toilet stalls immediately after this colleague had spent the morning scouring them to a shine, the clearly troubled High Financier then getting on the phone to report on the 'state of the jacks' to our supervisor. I could have done without this tale, as I could have done without this colleague's tears as he recounted it outside the Facilities yard where he had just been escorted by security. This was after his dismissal for incompetence and/or a lack of diligence in his duties, with no doubt the usual Irish charge of 'humourlessness' thrown in. I believed him (why would he lie?) but could do no more than commiserate wordlessly as he sobbed with Slavic abandon, shuddering at what might lie in wait for me. If a son of Kaunas, second city of the once-invincible Lithuanian Empire could provoke such an action, what chance had I, a mere Vistulian?

*

There are nine million Vistulians. From where most of us live on the Central Plain, one can look in almost any direction and see the imposing, snow-capped peaks of our mountain ranges, Wilma to the east, Zorno to the west; Uncle and Auntie. We say that as long as Uncle and Auntie are looking over your shoulder, you know you are in the right place.

From my floor, I can look south to the stunted hillocks the Irish call the Dublin Mountains. I do know, however, that out there behind the blinking lights in the foothills and in the south Dublin suburbs below them, as surely as my ancestors believed of the misty peaks of Uncle and Auntie, that there now indeed the gods do dwell.

Talcum powder, I have found, is a near-impenetrable deodorant; a tip I often pass on to new recruits.

*

This member of staff chose a *Happy Friday* to conclude his business. I must confess that, despite my ideological disapproval, my mood is usually lightened by the evidence of what must be an infectious atmosphere here during the celebration of, well, Fridays. The empty wrappers and boxes of candies and pastries left on shared work surfaces; confectionery often originating from the most exotic of politically stable destinations. Chalzatt, in the south of my country, where one can live like a priapic emperor for less than fifty euros a month, is not yet among them, alas. Items of casual clothing (the wearing of which is permitted on Happy Fridays) protrude from drawers and lie discarded under desks. Leather jerkins, fringed Western jackets, porkpie hats, snakeskin boots all lie where they have been discarded soon after their owner's confidence was perhaps undermined by the harsh strip lighting, or a critical comment some time after the Full Irish Breakfast, also a Happy Friday-only treat in the FinCorp canteen.

It is also possible to discern, on Fridays, a spark of defiance in the reckless display of non-work-related reading matter, the glossy magazines and alleged 'best-sellers' left openly on work surfaces. The relentlessly trashy tastes of this presumably educated elite do give pause to a lowly Vistulian, but there are exceptions. I am holding out some hope for one Vincent Hennigan in Arrears Support. His copy of Ralph Ellison's *Invisible Man* has been lying under his intray for weeks now; spine unbroken but still, aspirationally at least, present. I like to think I can tell which one is Vincent in the black tie group photo pinned above his desk. Even with his eyes reddened by the flash, I am sure I can detect some intellectual rigour in the one on the far right.

I know this is not Vistulia, where one must place an order so as not to miss the first print run of Jesef Zlee's latest libretto, for instance, or where a swimming pool lifeguard might just now be opening a slim volume of Fontan Mentoyan's (my poems can generally be uttered in the length of time it takes to exhale two deep breaths). But then, how many barbarous legions does it take to produce a page of Seneca?

*

Frank Bell was the staff member's name and his work space was always noticeably Spartan, Monday to Friday, January to December. Except for the two photos, the always light intray and the thick wad of well-thumbed business cards, you might have assumed it was as recently and hurriedly vacated as the five spaces next to it. That and the single hard-drive underneath his segment of the open-plan bench he had shared with his former colleagues, the ones already processed by the outplacement agency. His Roneo closet and pedestal drawer remained unlocked and unused for the duration of his stay here.

The photos were presumably of his wife and children, a boy in his early teens and two girls a couple of years younger. There was a studio portrait of the whole family and a less professional one of the children alone on a motor launch. It was moored to the banks of a river or lake, and could have been taken at any time or in any place, even southern Vistulia, in early summer; harvest time still, I trust, in that part of the world.

*

The stalls: what is it about the toilet stalls and the people who work in this building? The ceiling panel had either been popped out by Frank Bell or had remained loosely in place after some repair work by forgetful contractors, revealing the sturdy piping above. How many days, weeks, months must Frank Bell have gazed above his head, after perhaps discarding the idea of the doorframe, strong enough for me to perform my daily chin-ups on, but at barely six foot from the floor, not really fit for his purpose? Did he cast around for other methods, the fifth floor window, the roof garden next to the boardroom, before spying the open panel, and concluding it was just possible?

To climb up on to the cistern and, after pushing the panel all the way through, another step on to the side of the stall to reach the piping and with the proper knot in the length of nylon rope from Dealz, (the wrapper discarded on the tiles below) a near certain conclusion, given the height and the distance out from the cistern, once he had made up his mind.

*

I didn't linger long in there. In fact, I walked right out again, before the door had even swung closed behind me. I knew right away what I had just seen and didn't need to see any more. Leaving my floor, I took the elevator down to the ground floor to find Sharukh, the security guard. He was surprised to see me, two hours before I usually handed back my swipe card. He was at his desk, a map of the city streets on his lap, memorizing them for his upcoming taxi exam. Like myself, Sharukh is a man who hates to be disturbed and I was sorry to do it to him, destroy his night like that, but it couldn't be helped. We had recently begun to exchange a few words before I left for the night, often the last man out. He had relaxed his defences when he realised that, unlike some of my colleagues and fellow-members of the once Great White Race, I myself am colour-blind. On the contrary, I admire and even envy the richness of his cultural heritage. Sharukh will never have to explain exactly where Lahore is or what the climate is like in Pakistan or why he migrated to *this miserable rainy kip.*

Even though Sharukh doesn't know it yet and certainly didn't look like it a few minutes later, standing there in his unpressed USSSec shirt, cloudy-eyed, licking his suddenly dry lips as I gestured at the Gents door while rigidly holding my ground outside, he is well on his way to being one of the millions of minor gods now in the ascendant. As a Vistulian, I accept I will never see those heights again. It is they who are running things now, or soon will be: Sharukh, his managers at USSSec, their clients at FinCorp, the board of FinCorp's parent conglomerate, and ever upwards, out of sight of the rest of us, even of a Fontan Mentoyan. Yes, even the final actions of a Frank Bell will inject more juice and have more clout in the world he's left behind than those of a hundred Vistulians.

Even before Sharukh rushed back out of the gents with a stifled cry to call his colleagues and the authorities, I knew I was free to go. Even before they arrived and decided that, yes, the cleaner who found the body was contactable at any time and, anyway, it was all framed, dated and timed on the CCTV footage, I knew that the blessed obscurity of my weekend had been restored. My thanks to each and every one of them before I left, with my firmest handshake, was more heartfelt than they could know. I gratefully left them to manage the affairs of what is, after all, their world.

While I was free to go and find what poetry was left at the gable end of an empty barn at precisely 19.34 on the evening of 22 April 2018; or in the badger emerging later that same evening to march from his sett in those lost fields out on to a clear stretch of Vistulian highway to ponder the music of a humming pylon; or in those black storm clouds rolling off Uncle and Auntie, a site long abandoned by the gods, but beckoning still.

Máire Dinny Wren

worked in social housing in London before returning to Donegal where she now works as a carer to her mother.

When her first collection of poems, *Ó Bhile go Bile*, came out in 2011 Áine Ní Ghlinn noted that Wren had emerged as a fully-fledged poet. Her latest collection of poetry, *Tine Ghealáin*, received equal praise and follows Máire's first collection of short stories, *Go mbeinnse choíche saor*, both published by Éabhlóid.

Her work has featured in literary publications and in the short story collection, *Go dtí an lá bán*, published by Éabhlóid, 2012.

Máire received Duais Fhoras na Gaeilge at Listowel Writers' Week 2010 and Duais an Choirnéil Uí Néill in 2011. She won poetry competitions Ó Pheann na nGael in 2016 and Focail Aniar Aduaidh in 2017. An adaption of her story 'Thar an Tairseach' was broadcast by RTÉ radio and shortlisted for Prix Europa 2013.

Cosmhuintir

Nuair a díbríodh as a dtithe iad mhair siad sna heastáit thréigthe. Bhí siad beo ar an aer mar nach raibh bia le fáil. Cha raibh uisce le fáil ach an oiread mar go raibh an t-uisce imithe faoi thalamh. D'aimsigh siad tobar fíoruisce lá ach tháinig fear ó Uisce Éireann agus dhruid sé é. Dúirt na daoine go raibh tart orthu; níor thuig sé an focal fiú.

Tháinig fear slándála lá agus dhíbir as na heastáit thréigthe iad siocair nár íoc siad na táillí tí. Dúirt na daoine nach raibh airgead ar bith acu. Thosaigh seisean a gháire fúthu. Dúirt siad go raibh siad marbh leis an ocras; níor thuig sé an focal fiú.

Chuaigh siad ó bhaile go baile ar lorg oibre. Bhí ceirdeanna acu ach dúirt fostóirí nach raibh a gcuid ceirdeanna ag teastáil uathu. Shiúil siad na bóithre. Sheiftigh siad conamar bídh ó láithreán fuílligh a bhí ag dul thar maoil. D'ól siad as bairille a bhí líonta le huisce na spéire go dtáinig fear gardála agus thiontaigh ar a cheann é.

Shiúil siad thar dhroichead agus chonaic siad go raibh tuile san abhainn. Nuair a d'fhiach siad bolgam den uisce a ól, tháinig barda agus dúirt go raibh ceadúnas speisialta de dhíth le huisce a tharraingt as an abhainn. Chonaic siad bric is bradáin ina luí marbh fá bhruacha na habhna.

Shiúil siad a fhad le cé. Chuaigh siad ar bord soithigh. Ní raibh a fhios acu cá raibh a dtriall. Thit ceo trom agus chuaigh an soitheach ar seachrán. Bhuail sí na carraigeacha agus chuaigh sí go tóin poill. Tháinig siad slán as an tubaiste. Chuala siad bonnán ceo agus shnámh siad ina threo. Tháinig siad i dtír. Níor aithin siad a dtír dhúchais. Chonaic siad seantithe tréigthe agus chóirigh siad iad. Threabh siad agus shaothraigh siad an talamh.

The Common People

When evicted they took to ghost estates,
living on fresh air for want of food.
The water had gone underground
and when they found a well, a man
from the Water Board shut it off.
They pleaded their thirst,
but he didn't understand the word.

A security guard drove them out
for non-payment of taxes,
and when they said they were penniless,
he laughed. They pleaded their hunger,
but he didn't understand the word.

They wandered in search of work.
As tradespeople they were told
their trades were no longer needed.
They walked the streets, eating scraps
from a dump that was overflowing
and drank rainwater from a barrel
'til a guard turned it over.

They crossed a bridge and saw the river was in flood.
When they tried to drink its water
a warden said they needed a special license.
They noticed dead salmon and trout
lining the banks of the river.

They walked to the harbour
and boarded a vessel.
They didn't know where they were headed.
The boat went astray in the thick fog,
struck the rocks and sank.

The people survived the disaster.
They heard a foghorn and swam towards it.
The people came ashore.
They did not recognise their native home.
They found old abandoned houses and restored them.
They ploughed and tilled the land.